To lovely Louise
Forever FAB
So wonderful to meet you
& look forward to our
next merry meeting :)
xxx

From Frightened to FABULOUS

The 8 Secret Steps to Unlock the Best, Most Vibrant Version of You!

Much love
Heidi
xxx

From Frightened to FABULOUS

The 8 Secret Steps to Unlock the Best, Most Vibrant Version Of YOU!

By HEIDI FOSSALI

Featured on SKY TV - 'Who'd be a Billionaire' for Sky Living – an eight-part series

Featured on UK's Channel 5 'How the Other Half Lives' – Monte-Carlo Edition with Ruth and Eamonn Holmes

Featured on RoadDog TV Productions – 'The French Property Show'

Featured in Monaco Life – 'Women of Monaco Life'

On the advisory Board of 'Noon' – Online platform Midlife Reinvention

Featured in Stylezza Magazine - 'She Who Dares Wins'

Featured on RivieraFireFly – 'Positive Mental Attitude'

Featured on Fit Over 50 Life – 'Mid-Life Reboot Intervention'

From Frightened to FABULOUS

The 8 Secret Steps to Unlock the Best, Most Vibrant Version of You!

Special ***FREE*** *Bonus Gift for You*

To help you step into the BODY and LIFE you desire, a FREE BONUS Gift for you ($497 Value) go to:

www.Heidireboot.com

Enjoy my **5 x Full Body Workouts for Beginners** and a **14-day Healthy Eating Plan FREE** to take you from feeling mediocre to **magnificent in 14-Days!**

average earnings. Testimonials are not representative. This book and all products and services are for educational and informational purposes only. Use caution and see the advice of qualified professionals. Check with your accountant, attorney or professional advisor before acting on this or any information. You agree that Heidi Fossali is not responsible for the success or failure of your personal, business, health or financial decisions relating to any information presented by Heidi Fossali, or company products/services. Earnings potential is entirely dependent on the efforts, skills and application of the individual person. Any examples, stories, references, or case studies are for illustrative purposes only and should not be interpreted as testimonies and/or examples of what reader and/or consumers can generally expect from the information. No representation in any part of this information, materials and/or seminar training are guarantees or promises for actual performance. Any statements, strategies, concepts, techniques, exercises and ideas in the information, materials and/or seminar training offered are simply opinion or experience, and thus should not be misinterpreted as promises, typical results or guarantees (expressed or implied). The author and publisher (Heidi Fossali) shall in no way, under any circumstances, be held liable to any party (or third party) for any direct, indirect, punitive, special, incidental or other consequential damages arising directly or indirectly from any use of books, materials and or seminar trainings, which is provided "as is," and without warranties.

What Others are Saying About

Heidi Fossali and her Strategies

"I was feeling tired, lethargic, and I'd lost my energy, I knew I needed to do something. It was a feeling of depression and self-doubt. I lost confidence to feel connected to anything…even to life. We started working together doing one-to-one fitness, no one, even me, would think I could do fitness, I loved the challenge and working just with Heidi. Talking to her and knowing she passes no judgement, ever. I began to push the self-doubt away. I really started feeling stronger. It also gave me the confidence to buy new, figure-hugging clothes, new make-up and even a new hairstyle. Now, I feel sexy, sassy, and I feel pretty good about myself. I walk taller, I feel slimmer, I look and smile at people, I don't try and hide any more under baggy clothes." "If you're feeling lethargic and unfit, don't think about it, do it, reach out to Heidi. Get your mojo back with Heidi, I promise, just do it." - **Barbara (Dorset, UK) Property Manager, designing new goals, feeling happy and positive about life again!**

"Heidi helped to guide me through a very dark period of my life. I felt rejected and alone. My husband had asked me for a divorce, I was totally blindsided. My boys were leaving home for college, and on top of everything, I was trying to manage all the signs and symptoms of menopause. I reached out to Heidi, I had heard, through friends, about her coaching and reinvention, reboot programs. She was immediately there for me, listening with compassion whilst understanding my fears, challenges and the numbness that had taken over. I learned to like and then love myself again."- **Linda (New York and France) Photographer, feeling fabulous, confident, ready for her next adventure!**

Heidi has been an inspiration to me for about two years now! Since my divorce, I have been yearning to re-create an amazing new life…and for me, that means change my mindset, get fit and healthy, update my look which includes wardrobe, hair/make-up, and even dating profile photos! Heidi is just so amazing at all of these – she has inspired me to "up my game", and therefore my confidence! Heidi is fun, a joy to work with, and has even kept me accountable with other life goals. Heidi is elegant, feminine, sexy, fit, and simply a beautiful person, inside and out! What woman wouldn't want to have a role model and a coach like her? Thank-you, Heidi. **- Josephine (New York, USA) Ex-executive, now in an NGO. Healthy, happy and rebooted…**

"I needed help in several areas of my life. I had lost my self-confidence, I was bored, my energy was low, and I wanted to refresh the way I looked. I knew I needed a reboot. Heidi came highly recommended by several of my friends. Her energy, enthusiasm, compassion and patience were so contagious, and she was incredibly caring, instructive and conscientious. She soon had me looking and feeling like a new woman. Thank-you Heidi!" **- Dawn (Nice, France). Small business owner and mother of 2 boys. Back in the driver's seat of her life!**

"I saw Heidi on social media and I reached out to her. I consider myself extremely fortunate that I found the most wonderful, inspirational, and highly motivational coach in Heidi Fossali. Having tried several other coaches over the last few years I still found myself feeling STUCK and frustrated where my life was. Heidi changed all that within our first coaching session, I soon realised she 'got me' at last I had found a coach who understood my situation. Heidi's positive energy and lovely personality are so inspiring yet she holds me accountable in a gentle way. I highly recommend Heidi's coaching – she really is the BEST! - **Pauline (UK) Research nurse and finally feeling 'unstuck'**

"I'm in New Jersey, Heidi is in France, so we worked together online. She held me accountable and kept me fit throughout the lockdown -- in fact, I lost 15 pounds. She encouraged me to stay on top of my game, hold onto my feminine and not let myself go. Today, I feel good about where I am and where I'm going because she gave me the tools I needed to be who I always wanted to be, and I couldn't have done it without her amazingly helpful fitness programs, styling tips and tricks. Without Heidi, I would never have changed!" - **Betty (New Jersey, USA). Financial Advisor and entrepreneur. Confident and loving life again.**

"I stopped hiding from myself and the world by working with Heidi. It was simple yet PROFOUND what she taught me as I relearned to VALUE and LOVE myself."

"You owe it to yourself to stop hiding in your life and have a reboot with Heidi. Work with her to break through your self-imposed limitations, restrictions and, yes, I will say it, rut.

Find yourself, value yourself, love yourself and get out of hiding in your life by working with Heidi.

Say yes to YOU.

"If you don't say yes to you, who will?"- **Christina (San Francisco, California)**

HR Manager, author and podcaster!

"Heidi and I worked together for several months, and gradually I began to uncover and bring to light the strengths I possessed and had 'left behind'. We worked on small and immediate goals to start. My goals and dreams had been smothered and pushed aside whilst raising my family, and Heidi encouraged me to reconnect with them. She was my midlife reboot coach. She helped me build back my self-worth, confidence and self-esteem. I found clear direction with manageable stepping stones that didn't frighten me. Heidi is one of the most intuitive, positive people I know and would hesitate in recommending her to anyone.

Thank-you Heidi, for being my 'flashlight' in that dark tunnel I found myself in."- ***Katie (Boston, USA) Entrepreneur, business owner and volunteer***

"Transformation and change are a process, and feeling happy with yourself is a gift you can give yourself through taking the right actions and working with the right person.

"Heidi is that smart, savvy person. She is an expert coach-guide who helped me unlock and ignite my sparkle."

"Heidi works with you to expertly pull your vision, insights and goals to your awareness. Her focus and skill to narrow in on what matters and create motivation and accountability for you to take action in the right direction."- **Jenny (Florida, USA) Public Relations, working towards new goals with focus and enthusiasm**

"Heidi helped me understand how to mentally feel good about where I am and what I want to achieve, she made me feel good and lifted my confidence. I really enjoyed working with her – all the fitness, the styling tips and tricks. She has a great personality and she cares. I started dating again and felt fantastic physically, mentally and spiritually. I felt put-together and confident to go out there and meet the man of my dreams." - **Jacqueline (London, UK) Secretary, looking and feeling fit and fabulous.**

"When I was first introduced to Heidi, I was in need of a massive refocus and energy boost. My three children had left home, my career had overtaken my life and I had lost my 'joie de vivre.' Heidi helped me unstick myself from the routines that were overwhelming me and to see clearly what kind of life I wanted to live. Heidi's energy is contagious, working with her, I found myself rediscovering my purpose in life! I thoroughly recommend Heidi you will not be disappointed." - **Fiona (Guernsey, UK) Executive, balancing life with focus and enthusiasm**

"From the very beginning with Heidi, I felt excited. Her coaching helped me to see clearly through the foggy state of mind I'd been in. Her energy is contagious and I felt myself regaining a purpose in life and a renewed confidence in myself. She helped me make small changes, rather than overwhelming me with targets that felt impossible to achieve. She encouraged me, always energetic and positive. I felt truly energized and happy after each session!" - **Amanda (Edinburgh, UK) Author, feeling inspired, focused and creative again**

"WOW, Heidi, I am just getting up….and my body is telling me I worked out and it feels good. What an INCREDIBLE day on so many levels. I feel like a child after Christmas, so happy and fulfilled with great memories of a fabulous day working with Heidi. Lots of perfect gifts to myself of a new wardrobe and confidence level. You are a true gift to me, Heidi. "You have made me feel good on the inside and outside." **- Jennifer (Los Angeles, California) excited, focused and ready for anything!**

MOTIVATE AND INSPIRE OTHERS!

Retail Price $19.95

Special Quantity Discounts

5-20 Books	***$16.95***
21-99 Books	***$13.95***
100-499 Books	***$10.95***
500-999 Books	***$8.95***
1,000 + Books	***$6.95***

To Place an Order,

Contact:

heidi@heidireboot.com

THE IDEAL

PROFESSIONAL SPEAKER FOR

YOUR NEXT EVENT!

Any organization that wants to develop their people to become "extraordinary" on the inside AND outside needs to hire Heidi Fossali for a keynote and/or workshop training!

TO CONTACT OR BOOK

Heidi Fossali

heidi@heidireboot.com

THE IDEAL COACH FOR YOU!

If you're ready to overcome challenges, have major breakthroughs and achieve higher levels, then you will love having Heidi Fossali as your coach!

Heidi is compassionate, and kind. She's sharing her experience and wisdom within her Life Reboot Strategies. She's the real deal. She changes lives!

For more information on Heidi's coaching programs

please go to

www.heidireboot.com

Dedication

It is with gratitude and sincere appreciation, that I dedicate this book to my wonderful family and in particular my daughters. Without you both, and the lessons you have taught me, I would not have the blessing of being where I am today. Thank you! I love you forever!

Table of Contents

A Message to You!

This book isn't going to solve all your problems but I hope it can somehow hold a mirror up to show you what you can't see, then you can choose to draw a line in the sand and step across with clarity, courage and confidence. I want this book to help reignite your curiosity, your sense of fun and adventure, and then reconnect with your authentic, confident, charismatic self.

It's so easy to lose yourself in the mix; to allow someone or something to hold the steering wheel of your life and make someone else responsible for your happiness. Your belief system shapes your reality and you can find yourself trapped, powerless, dissatisfied, and feeling invisible. You possess the power to change any limiting belief and replace it with a new one; it just takes awareness, desire and practice.

Simply put, if there's one thing life has taught me, it's this: all beliefs are a choice and can be changed.

Could this be the time now to make that sliding door moment happen?

More often, it's the things you didn't do that you regret more than the things you did.

This is your time, you deserve it – what do you want?

From Frightened to FABULOUS

The 8 Secret Steps to Unlock the Best, Most Vibrant Version of YOU!

"Let your intelligent, fearless, authentic self, sit centre stage in your life. Be the director, producer, and lead actor in your own life."

"Shine bright, let your confidence radiate from within."

Synopsis: Heidi is a woman who has done it all, she has lived a life guided by the belief systems imparted to her by her upbringing, come to a crossroads and chosen to reboot her life and rediscover her authentic self. Heidi is an ICF Certified Life Coach, Certified Personal Fitness Trainer, Nutrition Advisor and a Beauty and Image Consultant. Her personal experience, and her work with women around the world going through the same midlife journey, has led her to create the '**Heidi Reboot**'. The Heidi Reboot is her effective program for reconnecting with your authentic female self and taking control of your happiness. In this book, Heidi discusses the reasons that women get stuck in midlife feeling invisible, frustrated and dissatisfied. Change comes eventually and Heidi discusses her own experiences about how she came to the realization that she needed to be responsible for her happiness, and since then she has helped other women to do the same. The book takes us on a journey of rediscovery as Heidi shares her own tales of pre and post her divorce, her thoughts, clear steps alongside tips and techniques, helping women reconnect and rejoice with the woman they might have left behind. Heidi ends the book off with practical guidance for readers who want to refresh, reinvent or reboot, those who have reached the crossroads and want someone to give them the tools they need to make a success of their second act.

— Laura Cure, Editor

A Note to the Reader

I wrote this book for those of you tiptoeing towards the middle years, those surfing the midlife waves, and for those crazy gals, skidding out the other side!

I've created a solution to help you uncover the best, most vibrant version of YOU, on the inside AND the outside. If you need some support, a pathway to follow and/or a gentle push to fully embrace the amazing opportunities that lie in front of you then this book, and the 8 Secret Steps are for you. I know that self-discovery needs space, freedom and a curious spirit, and I'd like to support you on that inner journey. Buckle-up! - you're going to find direction, purpose, and the woman you left behind.

My mission is to help you find what it is that brings you joy, direction, enthusiasm, and purpose, living the life you desire and certainly deserve.

You're a fabulous, multitasking, often under-appreciated yet dynamic unstoppable woman. Your life is full of responsibility and challenge, you accommodate your different roles and the different hats you wear every day. Underneath those hats, you've got goals and dreams, you just need to have the courage to step-up, speak-up and uncover them.

DON'T GIVE UP ON YOURSELF - Your time is NOW! What are you waiting for?

Each Woman's Story is Different

You've got so much potential, and sometimes you just need to pause and re-group, reflect on what you want, build back your self-confidence and decide if you're happy thc way life is and if not, have the courage to make some changes.

Perhaps you want to reinvent yourself and go back to work, but you've lost your confidence and feel you can't compete in the workplace. Maybe your nest is empty, and the void is deafening. Perhaps you've lost a loved one, been single for a while, or you're newly divorced and the reality of being alone is scary. Or maybe you want to focus on finding passion and purpose in life, to wake up each morning with enthusiasm for the day ahead.

Or maybe it's just **"I'm halfway...now what?"**

The reality is we feel stuck at a crossroads, feeling scared by the void called our 'Second Act' as it beckons us on 'stage'.

You do everything by the book, the way it's always been done. By nurturing and managing everyone else's life, you've never really thought about your own needs. You're so used to serving everyone else... Suddenly you wake up in the middle of your life feeling slightly indifferent, you're left wondering when is it going to be 'my turn?' You're held back by fear and self-doubt, you fear change because it asks you to let go, and you're not good at that. You hold on and stick with what you know, even when it's hurting and holding you back. Not only that, you've been through a lot, and you deserve to be happy.

In those quiet moments, when silence can be deafening, you're unsure of how you feel. Is it fear of the unknown? – the 'what happens next?' Is it the 'not being needed' and a loss of self-identity? OR is it that question, the one that wakes you in the middle of the night, the one that you've avoided, dodged, hidden behind and ignored for all these years... "Who am I – really?" and "What do I want from this next phase of my life?"

It's time to put yourself at the top of your to-do list!

Remember that your life belongs to YOU and you don't need permission. You're allowed to take ownership of your desires and the journey you're on.

What I know for sure is, we all have the same fears.

You lose your self-confidence and self-belief. You ask, "why me?"- why the heck not you? Negative thoughts take charge and your 'not enough' grabs the steering wheel - 'not good enough, young enough, pretty enough, rich enough'. That constant, nagging inner voice that 'keeps you safe' by bringing in self-doubt on a handsome white horse to save the day and 'protect' you from 'trying' and potential failure!

Self-doubt and fear go hand-in-hand and can annihilate your self-confidence. You doubt you're capable and sometimes, you even doubt that you deserve it.

I understand, I really do.

I'm here to tell you there is more!

We all have something to contribute, something to share with the world, we're all completely different and unique. You're complex and multi-layered and it's time to peel back who you truly are. Some of those layers will be easy to uncover, others more difficult.

I want you to be aware of your inner power and to trigger the desire to uncover the life you love, in whatever form that takes. I want you to feel motivated to find something that you're passionate about, then just take it one day at a time. You mustn't forget to focus on your strengths and how much knowledge and valuable experience you possess.

Come on! I'll give you what I know, share my secrets, and inspire you to unveil what you need to live a life with purpose and fulfilment.

I want to inspire you to get back in the driver's seat of your life, holding the map, and take control of your future. You're going to wave goodbye to regret, self-doubt and fear and say HELLO to a life you love.

If you don't dip into what your intuition is screaming about, your heart is yearning for, or your head is contemplating, how will you ever find your purpose, how will you even touch the shirt-tails of your dreams? You need to take a giant leap and be ready to soar!

"Nobody can go back and start a new beginning, but anyone can start today and make a new ending." – Maria Robinson

Think of some key decisions you wished you had made a year ago that could have enabled you to shift your life to where you truly want it to be. Do you remember what stopped you? Now could be the time to make that sliding door moment happen - even if it's just buying a pair of running shoes and putting them at the back door, as a first step.

I'm sure you're grateful for all you have, after all, you know how lucky you are. But you want to get excited about your life again… right?

I'm certainly not suggesting you head off 'Thelma & Louise' style, but what I'm suggesting is that you put yourself at the top of your 'to-do' list.

So, let me ask you...have you spent the last 20 or 30 years doing what is expected of you, following the rules, pleasing, managing and accommodating everyone and everything in your life?

Were you so focused on your family, career, or what was most important at the time and nowr you're asking yourself questions, you know something is missing, but what is it? Maybe somewhere you're feeling slightly disappointed?

You're not clear on what you want, no-one has ever asked you and good grief, you haven't had a quiet moment to even ask yourself. Now self-doubt, fear and 'it's too late' are in the driver's seat of your life.

Let me just say, for the record, **You're never too old AND it's never too late!**

To be honest, this is a common thread I have uncovered with many of my private coaching clients: the notion that life is whizzing by... it certainly feels like it to me!

My clients tell me that feeling fulfilled and happy has not entered their head, they fear that if they stop, get off the life-treadmill, they have to ask the hard questions, and be ready to hear the answers.

The truth is: you owe it to yourself because the pill of regret is hard to swallow.

The other challenge is motivation and energy - both pretty depleted and when you look at yourself in the mirror you see time and lack of attention has left your body ready for a kick-start. You know you're in need of some self-care on the outside!

Hey, let me just tell you - YOU'VE DONE A GREAT JOB! You're a fantastic woman, mother, wife, director, manager, actor, lover, best friend, sister, housekeeper, daughter, chef, teacher, caregiver, and so much more.

Allow this book to initiate and motivate you to feel inspired and energized to look at yourself and your life. It's about believing you have something to contribute and share with the world, that inner knowing that you are valued and truly deserve the life you desire.

Are you ready to design your second act or next phase?

It's never too late to tweak, update, improve, revamp, reinvent or reboot you and your life.

It takes self-awareness to be able to change what's making you unhappy and to achieve self-acceptance.

I know you're ready, I know you have self-doubt... **I believe in you!**

You have everything you need inside of you to live a vibrant, purposeful life; it all comes down to the choices you make. Without identifying what it is you need, want, or dream about, it's hard to get there.

Life is full of possibilities, and nothing is impossible -- but knowing what you want lets you know where to begin and what to focus on.

Keep reading for the 8 Secret Steps to deeply connect with who you are and what you truly want. Because believe me, this is something I know about. Here's what my clients tell me:

"I'm not unhappy, but I feel blah. Is this it?"

"I've got to change something, but I don't know what, how or where to begin."

"My body has changed. I'm scared of getting sick, but I've no motivation to do anything about it. Why bother?"

"I'm frightened of getting old. Time is passing so fast."

"I want to find some purpose and meaning to my life and 'jiggy' things up"

"I'm scared of being on my own."

"I've lost myself/I feel invisible."

No matter what, or where your starting point, you're going to take ownership of your strengths, talents and desires and then get excited to embrace the rest of your life.

With clarity comes confidence, with confidence comes action. You'll begin to thrive as you reset your mindset, feel brighter, more energized and healthier -- basically, still you but better!

REAL transformation happens on both the inside AND the outside.

I'd like to inspire and motivate you to try new things, set new goals, to re-discover your passions and purpose in life, to ultimately unleash your "WOW" factor!

You'll uncover what motivates you and why, then create the strategies and goals to live an abundant and fulfilled life.

You have life, so you HAVE purpose.

All you need to do is align your passions, talents and what brings you joy, then decide how to share them with the world to find meaning and purpose and your authentic self.

If you're ready to leave self-doubt, dissatisfaction and feeling uninspired behind and instead embrace discovery, vitality and connecting with your "inner goddess" -- who has SO many plans for you – keep reading!

This book is going to walk you through the exact steps you need to:

- Understand who you are, your unique talents and how you show up in your life today
- Uncover what's holding you back and keeping you 'stuck'
- Identify what you want and how you want to feel in this next phase of life
- Design the stepping stones to a life with meaning, purpose, one that fills you with enthusiasm and joy
- Step in to a healthy body and lifestyle that includes a diet and exercise program so you feel strong and energized every day
- Look and feel beautiful with radiant skin, gorgeous make-up, and a wardrobe with clothes that flatter your body and show off your personal style
- Realize your potential and confidently create a life you love

This book is part memoir, part manifesto

I share the **8 Secret Steps** based on my own transformative inward journey of self-reflection over the last 10+ years. Now I'd like to share them with you, in a shorter, more focused and practical way, so you can kick-start the 'new and improved you' -- the one that you know you're so ready for.

I use these exact same steps with my high paying, private clients, along with my online group programs, and I know that many other people need them too.

My own story so far, has been one of self-discovery, reinvention, bravery and ultimately overcoming doubts and fears to build a new life on my own terms. It is so easy to 'lose' yourself, not to know who you truly are, to allow someone or something to hold the steering wheel of your life, making them responsible for your happiness. This was a big learning curve for me.

I'm the same but different now, and I feel inspired, motivated and totally qualified to share my knowledge, experience and life 'know-how' to help you uncover the best, most vibrant version of you, both on the inside AND the outside!

The life you live are the lessons you teach.

Through sharing my own story and the stories of others – **'from Frighteened to FABULOUS'** is a mix of personal memoir, life guide and handbook, it's designed to support you as you move into your second act - whatever it may be.

Let this book complement and elevate you to know that you, and your story, are unique!

D-Day: Hitting Rock Bottom

Frightened?

"Heck yeah!" beyond frightened.

"Just grab the girls' clothes" I said in panic. "Put them straight into that box along with any photographs and toys you see in their bedroom--and move fast."

My heart was racing, my adrenalin levels were soaring. Today was the day. D-Day. Today, I was leaving my husband and 12 years of married life, walking out on it all. The fear was all-consuming: what if he decided he'd forgotten something and 'popped home' during my evacuation, my exit? That was unthinkable, so I scurried breathlessly around our small, rented house perched on top of the hill, scrambling to pack boxes, all the while knowing that inside were the only things I was taking with me into the unknown, labelled 'My New Path'.

With what felt like my life squished into six boxes crammed into the back of my friend's van, I got into my car without a backward glance and followed the van back down the hill. My daughters had gone to school that morning with absolutely no idea that they weren't going back home that day. What a HUGE responsibility and life-junction I found myself at, way outside my beliefs, values and family blueprint with no roadmap, compass, or plan.

I think now, looking back, it begs the question: **What was I prepared to risk and change to find the freedom, love and happiness I knew I was missing?**

It happened back in January when I finally had the courage to tell my husband that I wanted a divorce. I felt unloved, stuck, and frustrated, and it had been like that for a few years. We continued living in the house together, which was stressful: him hoping I would change my mind; me trying to figure out how I was going to earn some money to rent a flat for me and the girls. I needed a job.

Then, one evening in September, while the girls were staying overnight at Grandma's house, there was a horrific argument that escalated into something both frightening and abusive. His anger was so intense that I knew I had to leave, but not without my children.

His rage drove him to actions that were unforgivable, so in my mind I had no choice: that's why I packed up those six boxes, picked up the girls from school and simply walked out on my life as I had known it.

Courage is not the absence of fear, it's feeling the fear and doing it anyway!

I remember how trapped and unhappy I felt in my marriage. I knew I wasn't going to reach my potential and have the life I wanted for myself and my daughters. I decided I wanted to divorce. After several years of compromising, ignoring and numbing my emotions, I made my decision that I wasn't going to sacrifice the next 10 years and 'sit and wait' until my daughters left for college, to 'sit and wait' for my 'happy.'

Four years before that fate-full day when I left, we had moved to France and now, after a frantic exit, I was on my own with my two young daughters (aged 10 and 8). I spoke very limited French, and had been financially dependent on my husband whilst raising our daughters. This meant that I left with very little money and nowhere to live.

I was 42 and starting from zero.

At the Crossroads of the Unknown

I was going into unfamiliar and uncomfortable territory; I was going into the unknown on my own. We all have choices and I wanted my daughters to understand that on the other side of the life-changing decision I was making for myself and for them, I was choosing happy!

I didn't want to live an unfulfilled life because of fear – fear to speak up or of the unknown.

I had to make a choice, I had to dig REALLY deep for courage, bravery and determination because those voices in my head were constant and deafening, telling me: "You're not capable, you'll never change, you're not strong enough, you can't create something for yourself" believe me they were always there and on high volume.

And so began my journey – the one that has given me the clarity, life purpose and mission I have today to inspire and support YOU to reconnect with the person you might have left behind or the one you'd like to discover or uncover, then move wholeheartedly into your next life-phase with energy, confidence and purpose.

"Your life is a gift and yours to live fully with joy, passion, and conviction, so choose to be happy… it's a decision."

There were many sleepless nights, waking up in a cold sweat with overwhelming fear, the unknown was straight ahead, and I had no roadmap. At times, I found myself on my knees, praying at the foot of my bed for help, guidance, and know-how.

I look back and think how courageous (or plain irresponsible) my decision was and realize how challenging, yet transformational these years have been.

I've learned, experienced and gained such personal growth, what I know for sure is:

uncertainty is inevitable, no matter what, where or when, but the unknown could turn out to be AMAZING!

As these last years have unfolded, I've experienced some amazing highs, some crazy 'somebody pinch me' moments, along with some very challenging lows. From Monaco to London and Los Angeles to St Tropez, my life has taken me from emptiness, unhappiness, and the trials of divorce, to a fulfilled, passionate creative life.

To be honest, I didn't have a plan, I didn't know what I wanted from this new single life I had chosen. I knew what I was good at, my strengths and talents, then once I started meeting new people my life changed. Imagine my excitement when Sky TV featured me on Sky Living's 'Who'd be a Billionaire' an 8-part series talking about my role as Creative Director in party planning for the super-rich, which led to working with superstars Sting, Seal, Tom Jones, Nicole Scherzinger and Jessie J - are you kidding! - keep reading, I'll explain.

Then I was asked to be the presenter of the pilot series 'The French Property Show' and then a year later was featured on Ruth and Eamonn Holmes 'How the Other Half Live - Monaco' for the UK's CHANNEL 5 relating to the event planning business…truly unbelievable!

Living in the South of France amongst the glamorous and uber rich, I found myself working backstage as a stylist with the Formula 1 drivers for the 'Amber Lounge' event during the Monte-Carlo Grand Prix with supermodels Tereza Maxovà, Petra Nemcovà and driver's wife, Cora Schumacher. During the Cannes Film Festival, I worked as a stylist with Victoria's Secret models Ana Beatriz Barros and Karolina Kurkova. It was all breathtaking and mind-blowing.

My knowledge, experience, and passion for everything Faces, Fashion, Fitness and Fulfilment, along with a powerful mission to support you on your journey, inspired me to create my own consultancy as a Life-Reboot Coach.

I've had the privilege of coaching some amazing women in the US and Europe, women who have transformed and rebooted their life with me. I'm so grateful for their trust, honesty, and the vulnerability they've shown me.

What I know for sure is: anyone can change their life if they know what they want. When you focus and direct your energy, you can do and achieve anything.

Today, I am an ICF Certified International Life Coach, ELI-MP (Energy Leadership Index Master Practitioner), a Certified NASM-PT Personal Fitness Trainer, Nutrition Advisor and a Beauty and Image Consultant

Step into the body and life you desire.

Trapped in your B.S. (It's not what you think!)

"Just be normal like everyone else," I remember my parents saying on more than one occasion when I was younger, I can't remember what I'd done or said that caused this response. What I do remember is feeling deflated and annoyed, wondering why I had to fit into a mould of what other people thought was 'normal.'

I truly believe I've been struggling in that straitjacket of 'normal' ever since. I've been fighting against those instructions, consciously or subconsciously, for the last 40 years. I was never encouraged to believe that there was something extraordinary within me or that I could live way beyond the ordinary.

Here's the truth: you're an adult, you can write, rewrite and throw out any rules, any beliefs that you're hanging on to, you can ditch them, swap them any time, any age without needing anyone's approval. They're not brittle and written in stone – they are flexible and fluid, and they can change... It doesn't matter what other people think is true, it matters what you believe.

Your belief system (B.S.) shapes your reality, and you can find yourself trapped, powerless, dissatisfied, and feeling invisible. You can change any limiting belief and replace it with a new one; it just takes awareness, desire and practice. Simply put, if there is one thing life has taught me, it's this: **all beliefs are a choice and can be changed.**

My belief system kept me quiet, stuck in a marriage and playing by the 'rules', unable to share my true feelings with anyone. There was always the fear of speaking up and disrupting the norm. I was given the wrong 'instruction manual' and I've been weighted down with dogma and a belief system that didn't belong to me. My blueprint and life-roadmap were based on the beliefs and values that were given to me by my parents (who've been happily married for 64 years), alongside the environment in which I grew up. With this blueprint, my mind had been conditioned to live, believe, and value certain things that totally directed my life.

For the most part, these are good things. Beliefs and values give you an anchor, structure and 'instructions' for life; they teach you 'how' to live, to find your place in the world and what you believe, need, and value. I never questioned, nor realised, that it was totally possible to create my own reality and the rules and boundaries to live by.

Your beliefs can either support your dreams or limit them, they create the framework of your life.

My life's crossroads resulted in a divorce that was dramatic and life-changing, but maybe for you there doesn't have to be a ground breaking decision or even a crossroads. Maybe it's just a slight nudge that keeps reminding you of something that needs your attention, or perhaps that inner voice periodically telling you to pause for some self-reflection and focus. We can all feel lost, invisible, and dissatisfied at certain times in life, and it's important to never give up on yourself. Never ignore that inner voice because 'she' got the memo, and 'she' knows what to do.

If you get to a crossroads in life and find yourself muttering "there's got to be more than this" or you feel like you're in the wrong lane in life; or it might be that the road ahead is a scary void that you don't know how to fill – you have to stop, be silent and trust yourself because you have the answers already inside of you.

Patience is required, another thing I lacked back then. I remember how much chaos and noise surrounded me during those challenging times. My fear, my need to be noticed after feeling invisible to my husband, it made life noisy. I believed the more I DID, the more I would BECOME. I was shouting, he was shouting, all for the same reasons – to be heard, to be appreciated, to be seen, and ultimately to be loved. I was unable to be still, quiet or calm.

Once you feel calm and quiet, you'll be able to refocus and decide what you want, then get excited to embrace the rest of your life.

Don't Play Safe

I believe that at certain periods in life, you need to step away from the security of the familiar. Playing safe is instinctive, but sometimes you need to try something new. It's too easy to 'go-with-the-flow' doing it the way it's always been done, and suddenly you find that you missed the curve and time moves on!

- Are you procrastinating or putting off doing something, and now you need to take action?
- Are you feeling blocked or shut down because you're overwhelmed and need some clarity?
- Do you have a dream or goal, but feel helpless to reach it?

Take some risks – once you've made a decision to make a change, look forward and don't look back… what was, is over. What's NOW is what matters, and the possibilities for living a happier and more interesting life is in your hands.

GRAB that opportunity, that decision that could alter your destiny. Don't play safe, sticking to what you know.

There have been several turning points in my life when I knew I needed to make change in order to feel happier - a job, a relationship and ultimately my marriage, but I was scared. For months, even years, I stayed where I was, doing the same thing, at least I didn't have to worry about the "what-if" or the scary unknown.

We fear change because it asks us to LET GO, and we're not good at that. We hold on to the past even when it's hurting us.

We need to be aware that those 'four walls' that keep us safe and secure can, at the same time, trap us from life adventures and new experiences.

Change is inevitable, it can be scary, daunting -- and to be honest -- often debilitating.

Things like:

- I just graduated from college, I don't have a passion, nor a job
- I just got married and am anxious about the adjustment and compromise
- I just had a baby, left my career and don't know who I am anymore
- I want to get back into the workforce and realise I don't have the self-confidence
- I want to change careers, scared it's too late
- I've got 20 good years left, better crack on
- My mother just died
- I just got divorced
- My parents are aging
- I've just retired and lost my identity.

The power of uncertainty is infinite possibilities

Client Case #1:

Pauline contacted me through social media. She had seen me on the UK's Channel 5, when Ruth and Eamonn Holmes interviewed me as part of a series called, 'How the Other Half Live' – Monte-Carlo. At the time, I was designing elaborate parties for the uber rich on the French Riviera (as I said earlier, I will explain).

For several years Pauline had a dream to live in the South of France, she'd visited a few times and knew her ultimate dream was to move there.

Pauline, 64, lived in the North of England, she had been working as a nurse for 40 years and was the owner of a 3-bedroom house – this was her 'last chance' to make it real and so, on a cold rainy day in England, Pauline called me to share the vision she had, of her future-self living on the French Riviera. She knew I was a Life-Reboot Coach and was living exactly where she wanted to be... sounds like a perfect partnership to me!

Once I kicked the "I'm too old and it's too late" nonsense to the curb, she hired me as her coach and we were 'off to the races!'

We began weekly coaching sessions creating stakes in the ground, strategies and a strict 'to-do' list. There was plenty of fear and self-doubt that we consistently had to manage. She had to sell her house to create more financial security, the house had been on the market for over a year at that point, so we faced some challenges.

Over a period of 10 months, Pauline sold her house, took a one-year sabbatical from the hospital where she worked (she needed a safety net), packed and boxed up her life in England and arrived in Nice with me and my friends squealing with joy, holding a bunch of balloons and a huge sign that said 'Welcome to France!'

She had found a flat to rent so after dragging her two BIG suitcases up the stairs we popped one -- ok it was two -- bottles of champagne to celebrate - Pauline had done it! She'd left her safe, predictable, and secure life and stepped out of her comfort zone to realise her dream!

Pauline wanted to work part-time in France, and she found a job through an online platform working with English residents in retirement accommodation.

It certainly wasn't easy for her. I remember the selfie she sent onboard the EasyJet flight from Manchester to Nice, looking very pale with a 'Oh my gosh, what have I done' grin on her face.

I would love to tell you that Pauline lived 'happily ever after' in the sunshine in France BUT, the pandemic hit a couple of weeks after she arrived and France went into lockdown, the job she was going to start the following month was cancelled and on top of all that, she was concerned for her own health and being stuck indoors, indefinitely, in a new country.

It was totally understandable, she returned to England, found a beautiful, well located flat to rent and went back to the hospital where they welcomed her back with open arms – not surprising under the pandemic conditions. The experience created an inner confidence that Pauline hadn't felt before, now she feels empowered, in control, and ready to set new goals AND knows, she's never too old and it's never too late!

The takeaway from this is: The courage and conviction Pauline showed was impressive: she didn't 'play safe' she chose to follow her dream and step out of the 'ordinary' and the four walls that were 'keeping her safe'.

Light the fire within and transform your life.

Pauline remains a coaching client of mine today and we're currently working on another one of her goals - watch this space!

Here's your homework – starting tomorrow, repeat each day the AFFIRMATION - 20 times throughout the day – because there is power in positive, uplifting words:

MONDAY: I'm doing my best with what I have right now

TUESDAY: I have the power inside to make the changes I desire

WEDNESDAY: I'm smart, competent, and capable

THURSDAY: I'm growing and changing for the better

FRIDAY: I believe in myself and my abilities

SATURDAY: I can do anything I set my mind to

SUNDAY: I am getting stronger every day

Perhaps now it's time to share the story that took me 'from frightened to fabulous!'

My adventures and 'trailblazing' began at the age of 16. First time away from home,

I boarded a plane to Long Island, New York, for a week of orientation and then flew to Yuma, Arizona where my year as an exchange student began. My host family was waiting for me at the airport and then, a week later, I arrived at Yuma High School as an English exchange student. I loved it.

I had grown up watching American TV and now suddenly, it felt like I was living it! I chatted and giggled with new friends between classes at my school locker, I had cheerleading practice after school, football games on Friday nights and the High School Prom along with Graduation to end the school year! I took several classes at Yuma High and also enrolled at the hair and beauty college in town.

I learned a lot that year, broke the rules, and even broke the law once or twice. I started to uncover who I was, and while I was naive to begin with, I learned through trying and testing, by pushing and bending the boundaries and beliefs given to me.

By leaving the family nest, I was able to start figuring out who I was. It's challenging to 'spread your wings' in the playground where you grow up; you can never ultimately 'shake off' the family identity and unpack and discover who you are. I know that this experience planted the seed and the need for adventure, discovery and 'newness'. I think I was trying to get away from the dogma and limitations of the life and track I subconsciously must have seen ahead of me.

ACTUALLY…

It was at the age of 18 when I TRULY got my ticket to freedom, adventure, FUN and independence!

"Absolutely ridiculous," were the first words Dad said when he heard me explain what I wanted to do. "You don't even speak French!" he added, which was the truth. But I knew I wanted to go: a summer adventure in the South of France - that's what I had set my heart on doing, and yes, curiosity, wanderlust, and naivety were driving this 'trailblazer in the making'.

My Dad had an old friend called Albert, an elderly gentleman living alone with his dog in Menton, the last town on the Côte d'Azur before Italy. He "kinda-sorta" knew me as one of Dad's four daughters, but that didn't stop me asking him if I could come stay. "Oh, and by the way, I will be arriving next Thursday, and would he please pick me up at the train station in Menton at 5.30pm? PS: I'm the blonde one with big hair, wearing jeans and a yellow t-shirt!" … he had no idea!

So very reluctantly and with words like "irresponsible" and "you haven't got any money" Dad went with me to buy my ticket, leaving the next Wednesday, destination the French Riviera.

The unknown was beckoning and I was hooked!

I woke up at 4am that Wednesday morning, and both Mum and Dad drove me to the local coach station in Torquay. There, in the dark, with my small-ish suitcase, Dad with tears in his eyes, not sure if they were of joy, sadness or fear, I boarded a National Express coach heading to

London and then a train to Calais. From there, I took a ferry across to France, and another train through the night. I had booked one of those couchettes (bunk bed) – which somehow, I never managed to find, but that's another story! The final leg of the journey saw me on another train to Menton, and, I desperately hoped, to Albert – fingers crossed!

Before I left home, Dad had given me £100 in Travelers Cheques (which was one way to travel with money – back in the day) plus £100 in cash. It should have seen me through, but somewhere along the endless travels, someone stole my Travelers Cheques. But hey! – I would figure something out once I got to the Côte d'Azur!

It was a miracle but somehow, as the train pulled into Menton, there was Albert with his dog waiting for me on the platform. I knew he neither remembered nor recognised me, but he was so incredibly polite and kind, just such a lovely man.

Drifting off to sleep that night on Albert's couch, I knew I had to find a job pretty pronto. There was only £50 left in my pocket, and I had no idea how I was going to explain the robbery of the Travelers Cheques to Dad, as those words "irresponsible" and "you don't have any money" rang in my ears as I closed my eyes.

The next morning, Albert sat me down.

"Do you speak French?" he asked.

"Not really," I said as he frowned and anxiously scribbled out a list of potential places for me to look for my summer job.

"Oh no!" he muttered, shaking his head.

"Will that be a problem?" I asked with wonder. My naivety and enthusiasm had taken charge. The confidence of youth!

We had decided that I had to take my one pair of white high heels, my red trouser suit and big coiffed blonde hair to Monaco, where I was more likely to find a job in that "international playground," as he called it. I couldn't help but smile.

"Now you're talking!" I said to myself.

With no job prospects or interviews, I had no choice but to wing it. And that's exactly what I did. I sashayed up to the employee's entrance at the Loews Hotel in Monte-Carlo and announced to the security guard in no uncertain terms that I had an interview at 10.30am and would he be so kind as to let me in immediately. Incredibly, it worked! After listening to me babbling in broken French, he gave a sigh of exasperation and shushed me past.

"I'm in!" I whispered between clenched teeth. "But now what?"

My next step was to get an interview. I climbed the stairs, saw a door labelled 'secretaire' so decided to try my luck with the secretary. She was an uptight French woman and I had to invent a plausible story about an interview that had been 'arranged' for me at 10.30am today for my summer job at the Loews Hotel, Monte-Carlo. Reality was, I was lying through my teeth and there was no interview.

With the irritation that the French are so good at, she flung an application form at me for no other reason than to stop my persistent reply: "It's not possible, I have an appointment, you must have made a mistake!" I filled in the application with the English/French dictionary hidden in my bag.

First question 'NOM?' Damn it, what does that mean? Oh NAME, of course! Yes, I can do this.

And so, there I was the following week getting fitted for my uniform.

I had been offered a job as a cocktail waitress in the Lobby Lounge at the Loews Hotel, Monte-Carlo.

It was probably due to all the 'experience' in the hospitality industry that I had listed on my application. Truth be known I had NONE, but hey, they were happy to believe it, and I was happy to be given the job!

A knee-length red skirt, white blouse, red waistcoat, black skinny tie. All very smart. I had been told to wear comfortable black shoes which of course I didn't have, nor did I have the money to buy a pair, so, Albert very kindly lent me the cash and I bought a great pair of black, medium-heeled shoes – which crippled my feet for the rest of the summer.

I worked from 6pm-2am five nights a week as a cocktail waitress. I was that girl balancing a tray full of sexy cocktails for those thirsty zillionaires needing refreshments after cashing in their winnings at the fabulous Monaco Casino.

I DID IT!

And dear Albert was amazed, baffled and happy for me.

After my first month and first pay-check, I happily put the word out that I was looking for a flatmate, as I knew that Albert was more than ready to have this 'whirlwind' move on so that he could get back to his quiet life.

I moved in with Sophie, who worked in one of the restaurants in the hotel, and we had many adventures and 'close calls' that summer. It was a learning curve for me, to say the least, and let me tell you that those French girls taught Heidi, from that small seaside town in England, quite a few tricks, that's for sure!

Entering the canteen before my shift, I noticed a rather delicious looking French guy across the way. He was just so suitably moody, so cool and so French. I picked up my coffee and croissant and meandered over to a table where a friend was sitting who spoke English – conveniently close to the dashing monsieur.

His name was Jean-Pierre; of-course it was! Our first date was at the open-air cinema in Monaco, where we sat holding hands under the balmy Mediterranean skies sipping a glass of white wine. The film was *A Passage to India,* and I fell asleep. Whether it's because the film was so damn long or if I was simply exhausted from working so many shifts, but yes, I fell asleep on my first date with the yummy Jean-Pierre…

Fast-forward 10 years and Jean-Pierre and I got married in Los Angeles at the Sherwood Country Club. It was a stunning location and a gorgeous Hollywood style wedding – but wait, sorry, I'm jumping ahead!

I had the most amazing summer, fell in love, experienced some crazy times, watched princes, prostitutes and pop stars flow in and out of the lobby lounge, served many cocktails, danced many a night away, laughed, loved, and then, as the lights dimmed in Monaco at the end of the summer, with tears in my eyes, I left to go back to England.

Of course Jean-Pierre and I promised to stay in touch. I had my pockets full of business cards and scrap paper with names, numbers and addresses of amazing people I had met. "If you're ever in my area, please look me up, come and stay a while," they all said. "And why not?" I thought, "I just might!"

Back home in England I returned to my hair and beauty training, began working for my Mum's best friend at her salon and spa and I really enjoyed it. This lasted about 18 months and then those feet began to itch again and I knew I needed to hatch a plan for my next adventure.

So, this 20-year-old trailblazer moved to London, found a flat-share and a job working for THS Music Management as a receptionist, photocopier, Girl Friday, and coffee-maker extraordinaire. The company had three owners and managed Robert Palmer and other famous artists, it was thrilling when a band like Frankie Goes to Hollywood or Chrissie Hynde from The Pretenders stopped by.

The owners would casually share spicy stories of when they were management for Marianne Faithful – not that I knew who she was at the time. I was running here and there booking flights, arranging hotels and drivers, picking up dry cleaning, answering the phone and making a gazillion cups of coffee for the 'team'. During the week I continued to work at THS Music Management and at weekends I headed to rock concerts in stadiums and racetracks to be a 'Marlboro Girl'… let me explain.

One random weekend I went with my girlfriend Sarah who had an audition to be a 'Marlboro Girl'… she asked me to go with her for a bit of support. What actually happened was, I decided to audition too when

I got there, hey! Why not! – Imagine my surprise when they chose me, but sadly not my mate Sarah - she was encouraging and through clenched teeth she managed to smile "No worries, it's fine with me." My job description was to decorate the Formula 1 vehicles and of course, the racing team, in my red jumpsuit, big hair and with the energy of a Formula 1 car!

I'd been rustling up a plan during those 12 months working in London, keeping it to myself, knowing there was a bigger picture. And so, after celebrating my 21st birthday, I decided to buy a ticket around the world for one year.

Ticket bought: first stop, Singapore!

After the initial shock, my Dad had wisely insisted that I book my first bed before I left UK soil, so I reserved a bunk at the YMCA in Singapore and off I went.

It was so thrilling to arrive somewhere so completely new with just a backpack and an address – let's remember there was no GPS back then.

I arrived at the YMCA and found my bed, and then headed downstairs to McDonald's with a book as a back-up in case no one wanted to talk to me. The place was full of young people travelling, just like me, dying to swap stories, and this was the beginning of a most wonderful adventure.

Onwards to Indonesia for a week and then to Bali!

Staying in youth hostels was the key to meeting the most wonderful people, making instant friendships, and then seeing those familiar faces at the airport as we all headed on to our next stop.

In Bali, I hiked up into the hills, walked in the rice paddies, peeled pineapples on the beach, visited the crazy, fun, night markets, was spun around in a mini bus as it screamed down dirt streets with the doors open and reggae music blaring – it was fantastic and I ended up staying for two weeks with adventure, curiosity and discovery my drivers.

After that, I arrived in Australia!

I had very little money by the time I got to Perth, so after finding my hostel, I decided to ask around to find a job. This didn't prove that easy this time round, as all the jobs, the ones for us 'travelling types', were already filled.

Ok, now what? I had just enough money left for one more week at the hostel, which was a gamble if I didn't find a job. Not enough to fly to Sydney, not enough even to take the train across to Sydney, but JUST enough money to take a Greyhound bus across Australia to Sydney. Three days and three nights on a Greyhound bus – not kidding – that's enough to separate the boys from the men!

Hours and hours passed, day into night into day. We occasionally saw a kangaroo, an emu or a wild ostrich running by, other than that, ZIP ZERO! Our occasional stops were in the middle of nowhere to buy food, otherwise there was no chance of a shower and no hope that the video player (old school) on the bus would work just to break up the boredom… we crossed the Nullarbor Plain – a very long, straight, piece of road across Australia – more than 1,000kms.

Arriving in Sydney looking and feeling like a destitute slug, I found the slip of paper a fellow traveller had given me after hearing I was heading there and it turned out that the woman I called to pick me up at the bus station was the sister of my friend in Bali's stepfather's brother… twice removed… maybe?

Anyway, she was kind enough to let me crash on her floor, and three days later pointed me in the right direction to find a job at the conference centre in Sydney. I started working the very next day as a waitress for large conventions. It was so dull; someone would shout, "Main course served" and we all delivered plates of beige food to very bored people.

I soon found another job through a temporary agency, one that tapped into my skills, strengths and passion for fashion. I was booked for three days as assistant to Jill Markham, the director of the FIA (Fashion Industry of Australia). Happy days!

This was definitely in my field. Each year, the FIA awards the best Australian designers their version of an Oscar. Jill quickly realised I was rubbish at anything remotely secretarial like typing and filing but was fabulous at answering the phone, organising the designers and their collections, booking the models, planning rehearsal times, accessorising the collections and being totally enthusiastic and thinking on my feet.

It was my version of *The Devil Wears Prada,* and what was supposed to be three days turned into three months. Jill and I were made for each other: on the night of the FIA awards, I was the girl crouched under the stage handing the golden statue to the stunning, big bosomed, goddess who then handed it to Clive James (a popular Aussie celebrity) who handed it to the winner! And what an amazing experience it turned out to be for me. I remained in Sydney for seven wonderful months, working in different places and loving every day.

Next stop: Los Angeles, California!

Now, to bring you up to speed, the scrummy Frenchman, Jean-Pierre, the one I shed a few tears for as my train pulled out of Monaco station, had gone on to finish university in Nice and then taken six months to visit California. His six months had turned into 15 years, he was still in California, as he never left.

We had loosely stayed in touch with the habitual 'Merry Christmas' phone call each year. I was dating half of London and he, the equivalent in LA. We both agreed to keep in contact. Anyway, he was still in LA as I was heading onwards and upwards around the world.

I called to say when I would be landing in Los Angeles, and Jean-Pierre was there, waiting for me at LAX airport. There he was in a convertible, sexy, black, grumbling, American mustang, cool shades, polo shirt, good hair, good shoes… there I was, backpack over my arm, dodgy flip-flops, scrappy hair, dodgy shorts and a dishevelled t-shirt.

But it was wonderful to see him again.

I soon scrubbed up and Jean-Pierre and I took off together, having loads of fun. He had a fantastic job and had no plans to return to France. His apartment in Santa Monica was great and Mike, his flat-mate and girlfriend were super nice. Mike was working in LA for the summer before heading to study law in San Francisco.

Jean-Pierre worked long hours, so I was left to hang out with his flat-mate or head down to the beach to create my own adventures, which of course I did.

Mike was a triathlete so would go out running, swimming, and cycling when he wasn't working. He was also a personal trainer working with clients in the evenings and I soon discovered this concept and decided to study for my ACE (American Council on Exercise) certification to become a personal trainer too. I gradually built my own business, working with clients in Santa Monica and Malibu.

There I was, in the 'Fitness Capital of the World' out running with clients on the beach, pumping weights in the gym and getting PAID! It was a dream come true!

Strengths + passion = purpose! (Part of the 8 Secret Steps – keep reading)

I was happy in LA, although at the same time it was not good timing: I was not ready for a life with Jean-Pierre just yet, as I had my own life to discover and uncover on my own. I didn't want to give up or take a detour on my own dreams to please and fill someone else's. I broke the news, promising to stay in touch – and then I left.

When you work out who you are and what you do, you work out what you need.

What I want to share with you here is this: you need to know yourself, your values, your beliefs, your strengths and what you love to do and when fear or uncertainty creeps in you mustn't give up. No quitting and settling.

Return to London!

Once back in London, I enrolled on a fashion retail course, found a flat and I was off.

My experience working for the FIA in Sydney during my round the world trip had highlighted and anchored my passion for fashion. The fashion retail course was just a foundation program and once finished I stepped into a job with a fashion distribution company in Mayfair, which I loved.

We were the distributors for luxury couture collections, connecting designers in Germany and Italy with top department stores and boutiques in the UK. Four times a year we invited all the buyers to our very smart offices in Mayfair, London, and wowed them with the new collections, complemented by our in-house chef's new recipes. I was in my element working with fashion buyers, hosting fashion shows, and sexy cocktail parties for all the womenswear buyers, definitely part of my skill set.

I worked there for two years then moved to a sportswear company for a year, both fantastic work experiences.

My main passion has always been health and fitness, so after three years in fashion I was keen to get back into the world of health and wellness. Not wanting to be a trainer in a gym, I decided to try a different approach.

I met with the beauty manager at a super chic, sexy gym in Chelsea, the smart, celeb area of London and explained my background in beauty, fashion and fitness. I was hired to increase the size and turnover of their beauty department, then a year later they opened a retail store and asked me to do the buying and merchandising. I also employed the sales staff and managed the sports shop and really enjoyed the challenge.

It's so important to live your passions to reach your potential. If you're unsure what they are, just be curious and recharge your desire to learn and try new things.

Once you rediscover or reconnect to your strengths, talents and the things that make you happy, your life will have meaning and purpose. Your passions are not random, they are your calling!

Don't worry if you've 'forgotten' how brilliant you are: keep reading because I've got 8 Secrets Steps to remind you!

John was very good-looking with big strong muscles, he was a personal trainer and such a hit with everyone in the gym – including me! We started dating in secrecy because of a rule stating that staff weren't allowed to date each other. In fact, that just made everything exciting and naughty with the risk of being 'found out.'

He was from New Zealand and was in London for a couple of years, a bit of a 'travelling type' so perfect for me as I understood his kind – so much so that one day when he said, "Hey, wanna' go travelin'?" I said "Sure! Where are we going?"

So… I'd never been to Barbados!

That distant friend of a friend's, mother's brother syndrome hit us hard on arrival in Barbados and John and I found ourselves sleeping on the veranda of a very creepy, old, dilapidated Bajan house, owned by a man I would describe with the same words.

Our plan of action in Barbados was to teach fitness at one of those fabulous, glamorous hotels like Sandy Lane Hotel and Glitter Bay. We looked pretty damn gorgeous…both of us blonde, tanned, him with the body of a Greek God, me with toned abs and long hair!

We had bought matching red swimwear: his were red speedos and mine, a skinny red bikini – and we were ready for anything with our portable speakers, music playlists and our synchronized aqua aerobic routine. How could they say no?

Well, they didn't! So, every morning, we hustled those unsuspecting hotel guests off their lounge chairs into the pool to take our aqua-aerobics class. The manager was paying us $10 per person in the pool so, you can only imagine, those poor hotel guests didn't stand a chance with our determination, energy and our rapid head count – even before they had digested breakfast!

We were supposed to stay three months, but got fed up after two. Back in London, our romance didn't survive without the balmy Caribbean haze, and the stark London rain washed away anything we had shared together under the Barbados sun.

Time for a new project. I decided to pull all my skills, strengths and passions together and create my own business. I put together a business plan and off I went to Barclays Bank to convince them to loan me money. They appreciated my plan, and loaned me £5,000, and I was off!

My idea was to bring together fitness, beauty and fashion – my three passions.

I put a tiny advertisement in the back of *Vogue* magazine and soon heard from a dynamic woman, who worked for Goldman Sachs on Fleet St in Central London. I went to the Goldman Sachs gym three times a week to exercise with her.

At the weekend we would meet at her very elegant home and along with her husband and their two young children we would head down to the central private garden where I had them all running, doing push-ups on a park bench and performing jumping jacks to the sound of my whistle! She had a busy social calendar, so I helped plan her wardrobe, I shopped for elegant gowns, did hair and make-up before events and she paid me well.

I had another client, a woman who had just had a baby, she explained that she no longer recognised herself, her body, skin, hair or even the life she was living. She didn't know which way was up and needed something other than pregnancy clothes in her wardrobe. In many ways, she was the perfect client for me and we had lots of fun working together. I gave her a complete overhaul, a 'Top-to-Toe' Reboot (keep reading as I share her story a bit later).

I also worked with a Greek gentleman who was as wide as he was tall. He flew into London each month and I would 'walk him' around Hyde Park.

Just another quick reminder – all you have to do is identify and align your strengths, passions and what brings you joy then decide how to share them with the world (and potentially make money) - this clarity will give you the confidence to begin taking the first steps to uncovering your purpose.

Strengths + Passions = Purpose

It was almost Christmas and so Jean-Pierre and I were due for our Christmas phone call – but this time, after chatting a while, we decided that we needed to 'step it up' – we needed to 'make or break'. So, we decided to meet halfway, in New York City.

I flew from London to NYC and he came in from Los Angeles. It was a wonderful four days together and by the end of the weekend we decided that it was going to be 'make' and I would move out to LA.

Four weeks later, I packed up and moved.

Los Angeles, California, here I come!

LA was great, it suited me perfectly. The positive attitude, the outdoor living, all those beautiful people with their beautiful fit, healthy bodies. Behind my English façade, I was a wheatgrass-loving, energetic, California girl at heart!

My travels around the world had opened up and introduced me to so many new ideas: the world of FACES (hair and make-up) FASHION (image and style) and FITNESS (exercise and nutrition) were my 'Big 3!' – I had uncovered my passions, and Jean-Pierre and I were in love!

JP was climbing the corporate ladder and was doing well. We lived near the beach in Santa Monica and life was great. I waved him off to work and then went for a run on the boardwalk. I soon began teaching fitness and building my personal fitness clientele again.

And then, just when I thought it couldn't get any better, I found a beautiful diamond ring cleverly hidden in my dessert among the strawberries and cream! "YES!" I said to Jean-Pierre, my eyes shining with joy.

Married in July, pregnant the following March. We moved into our first house in Malibu, a modest one, nestled in a gorgeous cul-de-sac very close to the beach. It was idyllic.

I was truly in my element. I loved my life, I loved my husband, and more than anything I loved being pregnant.

Unfortunately, I started feeling lonely fairly early on in my marriage, JP didn't communicate well and found going to work the safest place as there were no emotional demands or, what he considered, difficult conversations about relationships that I was trying to have with him. I remember focusing on the arrival of the baby to fill the void.

My daughter was born just before Christmas, and my parents came to stay and see our baby girl. Well… all I can say is motherhood was, and certainly still is, my most favourite role of all.

The days, weeks, months passed in a haze of enlightened baby bliss. I volunteered at my daughter's pre-school, enjoyed 'Mommie & Me' classes, bedtime stories, baked cookies, changed diapers, pushed the stroller to the Malibu Starbucks where my daughter played in the sandpit with Cindy Crawford's daughter and Dustin Hoffman's kids… that's how we Malibu peeps roll! I made the most amazing friendships with the other Malibu Mums and they remain my best friends today.

I jumped in with both feet, gave 100% as a Mummy. I got all the love, adoration, intimacy and joy from my baby, and I didn't need to look to my husband for those things and feel disappointed.

A year and a half later, pregnant again, my second daughter was born, and I was in heaven as our family now felt complete. Motherhood came very naturally to me and I was thriving.

JP and I focused on our daughters and to the outside world everything looked rosy. He had a good job and I was a full-time Mummy and loving every single minute of it. The great thing about living in LA was that the lifestyle there offered so many things to do, so I was busy all the time with my girlfriends, playing sports, my babies, social events etc. So much so that the void in my relationship was not as obvious as when we decided to move back to Europe

The girls were six and four by then, and after 10 years in Los Angeles we headed back to France. We knew we wanted to be closer to our families, although it was still a difficult decision to leave California.

Return to France!

As soon as we hit French soil, my husband changed.

Neither of us were really sold on the idea of moving back to Europe, but the continuous challenges with permanent residency and visas in the US finally pushed us to come back. JP was angry once we got to France. He had run away from this French village, and now here he was back to the beginning.

I was totally lost I didn't speak the language and we were living out of suitcases at my French mother-in-law's 800-year-old village flat. Jean-Pierre and I were arguing all the time and he would disappear all day and leave me and the girls to figure things out. I had no one to turn to or talk to.

French grandma's flat had two bedrooms and a box-room with a single bed. She kindly gave her double bed to my daughters, and she took the other bedroom, so JP and I were sleeping in the box-room. I was devastated. It was unbearable, so I ended up sleeping every night, for three months, across the bottom of my daughter's bed with a chair for my feet and a fan perched close by, I remember, it was so hot that summer.

All I kept thinking was: this isn't my life; what happened? Where is my husband? Why is he not making this better for us? I was in a country where I didn't speak the language, had no money of my own, and finding a job wasn't really an option.

My two little girls looked to me for security and consistency and I was feeling so frustrated. I had nothing to fill the gaps anymore, no friends or infrastructure, so the huge gaping holes in my marriage were staring at me.

I took the girls to the UK to see my family for a week. I spoke to Dad about the way I felt, and he told me, in no uncertain terms, that I had to go back to France to my husband… so I did.

I got through the rest of the summer on autopilot. Finally, by the end of the summer we found our own small house and the girls started at the local school.

Jean-Pierre was negotiating a new job and once he began working, he found his rhythm and felt more secure. The challenge was to get our relationship back on track. I have an in-built belief, given to me by my parents, that marriage and staying together is priority. They've been married for decades, so with that blueprint, I kept trying and trying to make the relationship work.

I would hear myself saying to him: "Just speak nicely to me," and "Just pretend you like me" whenever he was abrupt and rude to me – which was often – and I didn't know why because he would never communicate. Of course, I now know he was suffering, in his own way, just like I was.

I tried writing letters to explain how I felt; I spoke gently; I shouted; I cried on the phone; I asked for date nights, but he totally closed down and returned to his blueprint that had been tossed aside when we were living in Los Angeles.

Over there he had reinvented himself; no one knew him, so he could be the hotshot. But now back in the town, where he grew up and where people knew the family, he slipped back into the role he had always assumed there as a boy.

I knew I couldn't move back to England because JP wouldn't let me take the girls, they needed their Daddy, and my parents had already told me I had to stay with my husband.

One day as I waited to pick up my girls from school, I felt a tap on my shoulder, and I turned to see the most gorgeous smiling face and the voice of an angel asking if I was American, and shall we go for coffee with the children? It was like a gift from above! Her name was Sue. She was from California and had three children of similar ages to my girls.

This friendship was instant, valuable and it truly saved me.

We were inseparable, the two 'Americans' always annoyingly happy and chatty compared to the complaining, fractious French women around us! It was my safe haven of familiar, secure and so much fun every single day and of course our children loved each other too.

Sadly, my relationship with JP was suffering. The gap between us was widening, I was trying desperately to get his attention, but he was distracted while adjusting to this new life. Was it the new environment? Frustration? He'd changed. Had I changed? I didn't know. All I did know was that I wasn't happy, and neither was he.

I knew I was covering up an empty marriage, and by now JP was sleeping in the guest room. He was stressed at work and kept waking up in the night. With no intimacy in, or out of the bedroom, no communication except regarding the girls, and hardly spending any time together, our relationship was suffering more and more.

He made me feel stupid and annoying. I didn't like the way he spoke to me in front of the girls, and I certainly didn't feel loved. I was disappointed because I no longer felt like the vibrant woman I had left behind in LA. She was gone. How did I get here? I had no way out…so I carried on for another three years.

What I know now, and the MOST important lesson learned, is - **YOU are responsible for your own happiness.** It's so easy to allow someone or something to hold the steering wheel of your life and make someone else responsible for your happiness.

The truth was that I had given that responsibility to my husband. His blueprint and childhood were so very different to mine, and on top of that, he found being back in France very challenging. I wanted him to come to me for support, but his instinct was to shut-down completely, leaving me disappointed and unhappy.

I dared to utter the 'D' word to my friend, and it was scary. Divorce was the obvious solution, but I had no concept of what that looked like or the courage to act on it.

I remember thinking: how can I continue like this?

But how on earth could I change anything? Where would I find the courage to change my life?

I was trapped and it was not just my future I was thinking about, I had two little girls who loved their Daddy. Should I sacrifice the next 10 years of my own life and 'sit and wait' until my daughters leave for college, 'sit and wait' for my 'happy?' If I did that, they would be burdened with the reality that I did it for them, that I gave up my happiness to protect them – and I didn't want that.

I knew I wasn't going to reach my potential or have the life I wanted nor the life I wanted for my children if I stayed in my marriage feeling frustrated and unloved. I would be letting myself down. My story so far was one filled with adventure and discovery; I had pushed the boundaries and experienced so many amazing things. So, I couldn't sit here stuck like this.

Where would I go? I had no money and was dependent on my husband as a full-time Mum. Sitting with me all the time was an underlying, permanent sense of panic. I didn't want to just settle. I felt unappreciated and underestimated. I didn't want to give up on myself, let go of my dreams and ambitions and those for my daughters.

Christmas was coming, and my parents knew I was unhappy. I'm sure they knew what was coming as they packed their suitcases for Christmas in France. It was wonderful and such a relief to see them. The girls were especially excited. New Year came and went and then I dropped the bomb.

It was January 3rd, and to this day I don't know where or how I found the courage to speak up and say I wanted to divorce. My words on that day triggered a full-blown atomic explosion of rejection and abandonment inside JP's body and mind. His family background and a childhood with no father, splintered and littered with wounds and lack, were ignited and now sadly he was joining the dots of pain and suffering.

My childhood was very different: I grew up in a family with parents who are still in love after 64 years together. The words I heard myself mutter, very gingerly, were in direct opposition to the dominant belief woven through me. The one thing that I believed and understood to be the most important pillar in life was the commitment of marriage.

Growing up in that environment with the notion of 'playing safe' and 'normal' the driver for everything, became the belief, framework and blueprint of my life. There was no room for 'drawing outside the lines', it was all about 'grow where you're planted' and 'just get on with it' and no fuss.

I thought my parents would be more supportive, but they were so frightened that I'd be on my own with two young girls that they did everything they could to talk me out of divorcing my husband. They took away all my self-belief and confidence. As they saw it, perhaps accurately, I was being totally irresponsible with no game-plan, money or place to go. Yes, they were right, but it wasn't what I wanted to hear.

I felt annihilated.

It would have been much easier during those days over Christmas, with my parents both in tears as they begged me to reconsider, just to accept, accommodate and please them, to throw in the towel and give up on myself. I'm a pleaser, like many women, so this decision tested every belief and value I'd been given or picked up on the way. I was 42 years old, and my daughters were 10 and 8. How could I just back down and disappear?

I knew deep down there was something out there, something bigger, some kind of 'mission' I had to fulfil. I remember Dad saying, "What are you going to do on your own? You'll have to claim from the social services."

I was devastated. And also offended and upset. I remember saying, "Dad, I am so much more than you think! I have so much potential! I know I can find a new path for myself."

At that moment I remember taking a piece of paper and listing everything I had done in my life, up to that very moment, to show Dad '*who*' I was and to prove that I wasn't such a hopeless case, which is how he made me feel.

The truth was, I had no idea how hard it was going to be, it was that very naivety that kept me hopeful and determined.

The unknown was straight ahead and I had to step into it.

The early morning light would whisper through the curtains and I would ask my guardian angel for courage, confidence and some kind of sign to know what to do next. The uncertainty and unpredictability of my life fueled my actions and choices, whilst at the same time I had the notion and intuitive feeling that I was being guided by something or someone.

Never give up on yourself, never ignore that inner voice because 'she' got the memo and 'she' knows what to do.

We have a choice; and this was mine!

I wanted my daughters to understand that on the other side of this life-changing decision I was making for myself and for them, we all have a choice. We must choose to be happy, it's a decision. My life is a gift and mine to live fully with joy, passion and conviction.

I know that self-discovery needs space, freedom and a curious spirit. I wasn't going to pull the plug on Heidi, she might be feeling lost, but I knew I could find her again… I was going into the unknown on my own.

The anger, disbelief and denial bubbled beneath the surface for my husband for the next nine months. We were still living together in our small house, him hoping I would change my mind; me knowing I needed to make some money and find somewhere for me and the girls to live which meant paying rent, bills, food etc.

As a full-time mum, I relied on my husband financially, and now I wanted to change my life. Yikes! An important lesson here is this: you must always find a way, even whilst raising children, to make your own money; always keep some money for yourself as a 'runaway fund.' Yes, even if you're happily married!

The power of uncertainty is infinite possibilities

"Come on Heidi," I said. "If you want to change your life, you're going to need to find a job and fast!"

Monaco was my best bet with its international clientele. My spoken French was still very limited, so I needed to use my strengths and talents in an English-speaking environment. I had studied hair and make-up at beauty college in Yuma, Arizona when I was an exchange student and then again in England. I seemed to be good at it, so after some research I found 'The Monaco Wedding Planner.'

I called their office, arranged an interview, and was quickly hired as their in-house 'Hair and Make-up Artist'. My diary was pre-booked from May to the end of September. My mission was to 'paint and primp' stunning, very fashionable, international brides, to make them look and feel totally gorgeous on their wedding day.

Yes, I was working with my strengths, skills and passions; and I loved it!

Another of the Mums, at my daughter's school, had become a firm friend, so on that fate-full day when I got up and left, she kindly let us stay in her guest room. Shortly afterwards she offered me the rental of her small village house as her tenants were moving out. Did I want to rent it? With no plan, no possessions and only the money I had earned painting the faces of glamorous brides all summer, I said YES! We agreed on a modest monthly rent and the 'Three Musketeers' moved in.

The girls and I were so excited, this small house felt like a palace!

Thankfully the house was fully furnished because we moved in with not even a fork or spoon, no towels or sheets. Nothing.

I did it… I made it…we found our home.

I now had to re-invent a new life for myself and maintain the stability and nurturing that my daughters needed. Every day I chose to focus on my daughters creating and maintaining a loving, consistent, secure and supportive home life for them. They were, and are, the two most important people in my life and I am so incredibly happy and fulfilled being a Mum.

We had so much fun together in our 'palace' in the village. I enrolled them at the local school and they were happy. We cooked and baked together, painted our nails and faces, did homework and housework, sleepovers, read books, sang songs and loved and laughed together every single day. I was totally enthralled with my daughters – nothing could touch me or knock me off my perch as a mother. I was fearless.

"Difficult times can Diminish, Define or Develop us" – Jim Kwik

With the girls back in school and rent, food and bills a stark reality, it was time for me to dip back into my 'Mary Poppins' bag of skills and know-how. I had different hats to wear and passions to share, my challenge was to find and connect with people who needed what I was selling.

Winter is very quiet on the French Riviera, but Spring brings the international crowd, the jet-setters and those delicious young ladies drunk with wedding fever! That summer, whilst working as a hair and make-up artist, I met Pascal, a very handsome Frenchman who owned an events and party planning business, and we started dating.

The sexy Riviera vibe packed all the bars, restaurants and beaches along the coast. I had several weekends booked for weddings, and I met each bride and planned hair and make-up for their glorious day. I decided that this summer I was going to create a true business brand for myself. I created a consultancy called 'Bellissima-by-Heidi', a consultancy for the things I was totally passionate about – hair, make-up, personal fitness training, fashion and wardrobe planning.

I called myself a 'Lifestyle Beauty Coach'. I started networking and talking to people and for the next 12 months worked with photographers on photoshoots, several wedding and event planners. I created group workshops for ladies teaching make-up, fitness and wardrobe planning, selecting five pairs of jeans and throwing out 15, sifting through jackets, sweaters and shoes to fine-tune their overstuffed wardrobes.

Pascal had an ultrarich clientele and booked me on super yachts with zillionaires talking skincare, hair, make-up, and birthday parties. It was an amazing experience, fun and creative. I enjoyed working and playing in this decadent arena, but my challenge was in the middle of the night when fear struck and I could hear my heart pounding and would catch myself holding my breath. The reality and responsibility amplified, my stomach cramped with anxiety, I lay awake wondering how the heck did I get here? The juxtaposition of my life -- and nobody ever knew!

Back out on the field - Pascal worked each year for a wealthy family that visited the French Riviera for the Cannes Film Festival. An entourage of exquisitely beautiful women, and then there was 'Queen Bee' (wife of the boss). Pascal recruited me as her stylist and within a week I was being escorted by bodyguards on to their super yacht, then to their summer villa in Sardinia to give skincare treatments, apply make-up to breathtakingly beautiful women, blow-dry their golden locks and zip up their designer gowns.

It was another world!

Pascal asked me to design the birthday party for Queen Bee. My business card said 'Creative Director' and I loved it. Not sure how it happened but with passion leading the way nothing was going to stop me! I designed a 'Venetian Masquerade' for Queen Bee's 38th birthday.

I created the storyboard and theme for the event, and then the technicians and designers interpreted the 'story' and built the setting for the party. The big night arrived and flocks of sparkling, gorgeous gazillionaires arrived at the enormous villa they had rented for the birthday bash. I was there with the team, ready to pamper and adore the client, whilst I gripped my walkie-talkie radio that crackled with directions and a countdown from the manager… so exciting!

My creation had come to fruition.

It was an exclusive VIP party for 50 people. We had booked dancers inside bubbles floating on water, contortionists twisted on podiums, gymnasts wrapped in fabric tumbling through the air – nothing could be more amazing, that was… until I met Sting backstage! We chatted before he began a two-hour exclusive, private concert, followed by Nicole Scherzinger…WOW!

Queen Bee (as I called her) was a delicate, beautiful, charming, waif of a woman, along with her pale skin and perfect body she had given birth to five daughters and now THEY wanted designer birthday parties – so over a period of three years, as the 'Creative Director' and a Mum to girls, I knew exactly what to do!

I designed a 'Victoria's Secret' themed party – during the day it was a decadent, all-white, pool party followed by an evening fashion show, where the girls, along with professional models, strutted down the catwalk wearing huge, customized, designer wings. There was a 'Jungle Jam' party with a swim-up bar, real monkeys, parrots and snakes. I designed an' Ice Age' party in August with an outdoor ice-rink, snow, and icebergs in the pool, and also a 'Hawaiian Beach Party' with a sandy beach & volley-ball court (we brought tons of sand to go around the pool at the villa). We built a rock slide and booked authentic Hawaiian dancers to dance the hula. I designed a 'New York, New York' party and we built model skyscrapers creating the NYC skyline with boutiques like Tiffany's where the children could go inside and make jewellery!

I LOVED it!

The following year for Queen Bee's 39th birthday, I created 'Moulin Rouge' in the garden of their villa with a carousel, a Parisian skyline, vintage cars and a huge structure built in the garden as the Moulin. We booked a French can-can, a sexy tango and a girl on a swing, wearing nothing but pink feathers swirling above their heads singing "Diamonds are a girl's best friend" and we booked Seal for the private concert followed by Jesse J.

After the concert I went backstage to ask Seal if we could take a photograph together, and gracious as he was, he agreed! And here's a secret I want to share – and don't tell anyone… Seal and I exchanged contact details and met in London. He invited me to the recording studios! He was amazing and a perfect gentleman. We had lunch together in a private club close by and then went back to the studio where he played music for me. I sat with him as he recorded tracks for his new album – now that blew my mind… oh, and we might have kissed – twice!

It was right about this time when SKY TV contacted me through Pascal.

And that's when the magic happened!

Sky TV featured me on Sky Living's 'Who'd be a Billionaire' an eight-part series talking about my role as Creative Director in party planning for the super-rich!

I was on television! Can you believe it?

Let's just stop for a minute and check back in with reality here: no-one, especially me, could have imagined any of this could, or would happen to me. There were MANY times I was scared and overcome with self-doubt – I was like that archetypal swan: poised and calm on the surface, but paddling like mad below water!

All I know is that when you dare to step out of your comfort zone and decide to focus on what YOU want, create the intention, then good things happen!

Remember, your life belongs to YOU, you don't need permission. You can ignore the questions you ask yourself, or you can go in search of the answers: it's your choice. This is the beginning of your inner journey of self-discovery!

During this time, my daughters were blossoming and making lots of new friends and loving their school. My house was always full of giggling teens; my daughters, now 11 and 13 were thriving, doing well at school, playing tennis, enjoying dance class, both had lovely friends that would 'hang out' on our sofa.

My house and heart were always open and available for my teen tribe. I wasn't the 'average Mum' they told me! I always had music playing, my make-up kit scattered on the kitchen table and curling iron in hand. I'd lived in LA, had done some modelling, was a fitness trainer and had an exciting selection of high heels in my wardrobe. Need I say more?

I was in heaven. When your passions collide, it's like riding the perfect wave for a surfer or hitting a hole in one for a golfer.

For me…teenagers + teaching my passions + inspiring = my purpose and happy.

The truth was, I found my strength and confidence through my daughters…they kept me centred and empowered.

Bragging rights!

My apologies upfront for bragging… I'm allowed because it took a huge amount of attention, focus and compromise, along with plenty of hustle and asking for help, to make sure my daughters had the opportunities they deserved. They did brilliantly well at school and both graduated top of their class. Both went on to top universities in the US and UK. As a single Mum with intelligent daughters, my efforts worked and I was very grateful.

My elder daughter went to UC Berkeley in San Francisco as an undergraduate on an academic scholarship. After graduating she worked for a law firm in San Francisco for two years and is now a postgraduate studying law in Washington DC.

My younger daughter went to King's College London and graduated with a business management degree. She has a full-time job in London and alongside, is studying for her Master's at University College London.

Proud might be an understatement - I'm beyond proud of them both, to see how kind, intelligent, conscious and independent they are as young adults makes my heart sing.

I'm also proud of myself: I raised my daughters on my own, while ensuring they have a great relationship with their Dad.

I did my very best to give them a secure and loving environment to thrive, to grow, to be curious and discover who they want to be. I did everything I could to make sure they received the education needed to equip them for the road ahead and the amazing life they will create for themselves.

There's always a way forward. You can have what you want.

Time for my Next Project!

Here's where the idea came from: I wanted to take the decision-making out of my morning routine and the persistent question of "What to wear?" I thought that if there were one item of clothing, simple yet luxurious, what would it be?

My inspiration was quite selfish, I was thinking about what I wanted, although realistically, it was probably what we're all thinking! The answer came to me: it would have to be a simple tee-shirt, one that we could pair with our favourite jeans, or under a jacket for the office, with casual pants at the weekend or wear with a cocktail skirt for a party or special occasion! But it would have to be made from the most luxurious yarn in the world – LORO PIANA (the world's leading luxury textile company) using both silk and cashmere - a mix of simplicity and luxury!

You'll notice, I'm never short of ideas and they're usually BIG ones! The question was; How was I going to create a clothing brand, I had no money?

Throughout this period, I was still working as a personal fitness trainer and one of my clients was a successful businessman. He was also a 'business angel' helping entrepreneurs with their 'Start-ups.' So, after a particularly tough morning workout, when he was feeling exhausted and perhaps slightly 'weak' I pitched my business plan for a Luxury Tee-shirt brand?

Believe it or not, he said YES! And, by-the-way, he casually mentioned that he happened to know the big boss at LORO PIANA. Seriously, you can't make this stuff up!

It all came to fruition after I designed a capsule collection of eight tee-shirts. I produced them in Italy using 100% LORO PIANA silk /cashmere yarn and called the collection 'SIRO cashmere'.

My SIRO cashmere tee-shirts are your 'best friend' that 'take you anywhere'... available across 10 colours, all complementing the stunning back-drop of where I live on the French Riviera.

They are gorgeous! I really love the collection and I wear them year-round. **Check them out on my online shop – www.heidireboot.com**

Around the same time, I received a call from the UK's Channel 5. They asked if I would help them with their episode of 'How the Other Half Live – 'Monte-Carlo edition' with Ruth Langsford and Eamonn Holmes, two very popular presenters in the UK. I can only presume they had seen me on the series I did with Sky TV.

I was so excited and said YES immediately!

I worked with the producer along with my contacts in Monaco to create a super sexy episode and I was thrilled when Ruth and Eammon interviewed me on camera, and of course they wanted to know about the decadent parties of the mega-rich. Believe me, I had PLENTY of stories to share! It was FABULOUS!

Next *Stop:* Finding the Missing Piece

I've always had a real interest and curiosity in human behaviour and the psychology behind how we think, feel and act.

I had always focused on the 'outside' even my own outer self – the outer appearance – fashion, hair, skin and make-up even fitness has a huge aesthetic appeal. I wanted to add 'Life Coach' to my résumé and portfolio. I knew this was the missing, and final piece to my puzzle.

I studied for a year and finally received my Life-Coaching Certification and then created my Life-Reboot Coaching Consultancy. Now, I had the accreditation and expertise required to work in a totally holistic way with my clients… A 'Top-to-Toe' a 'One-Stop-Shop' Heidi Reboot!

I knew that with my insight, experience, knowledge and empathy, I could absolutely help others live their best life physically, mentally and emotionally, I also knew that helping someone with the way they look on the 'outside' is important but only if it reflects how they feel about themselves on the 'inside'. With these coaching skills and techniques, I knew I could empower and support anyone, to improve any part of their life, starting on the inside with how they were thinking and feeling.

I've unpacked and understood so much about myself, the WHO, the WHAT, the WHY and the HOW. With a strong sense of self and a desire to inspire others, I strive to maintain a 'never give up' attitude along with an inner-knowing that I have a mission and purpose. This has ultimately become the backbone to this book and the journey I took to unveil exactly what I wanted from the next phase of my life, the one that has led me to today. Now I want to help you do the same, with ease, joy, and transformation...from the inside out!

I want to inspire, motivate and support you to tap into your brilliance, and be ready to live your best life!

It's never too late to refresh, revamp or reboot you and your life!

It's my mission, purpose and the reason why I'm here - no doubt it's been revealed and reinforced by my life-journey. I know that any transformation has to start on the inside and is directly related to the beliefs and habitual thoughts, patterns and stories you tell yourself.

I want to inspire and support vibrant, intelligent women like you, to take an inward journey of self-reflection and discovery, so you can uncover what you truly want and create a vision for your life – (the one you desire but haven't yet allowed yourself to believe could be yours).

To discover, uncover or reconnect with the woman, you believe, you left behind and secretly miss.

I believe that REAL transformation happens on both the inside AND the outside… which brings me to TODAY and writing this book!

Get Back on Your Bike ...Just Start Pedalling!

Question: Why is it that we 'park' our passions and the very things we love to do? We either lean them up against the wall in the corner of the 'garage' or hang them from a well-positioned rack from the ceiling.

Well, it's time to unhook, dust off, oil-up that 'bike', that freedom to fly, that speedster for fun, frivolity and the future! Jump back in the saddle, connect or reconnect with who you truly are and the things that light you up and set your soul on fire!

"We don't stop playing because we grow old; we grow old because we stop playing" – George Bernard Shaw

I remember summers as a 9-year-old, playing on bikes with my sister Lisa, my neighbour Sarah and my younger sister Wendy, who was 5. We had a steep path in our garden (well... ok, it felt steep to me at that age!) and we used to line ourselves up, one behind the other. My little sister Wendy had one of those 3-wheelers with the foot pedals on the front wheel, and she just lifted her feet and went down as fast as she could, knowing we were all coming after her at top speed!

There were bushes, trees and a swimming pool at the bottom of the garden, so the fear of not being able to stop and hitting a tree, landing in the stinging nettles, or flying head first into cold water kept us giggling with fear, motivated by the unknown and elated by our survival – we did it over and over again!

Our clothes got dirty, our knees grazed and bloody after a few collisions and the occasional wipe out along the way. Up and down we went all day, and only reluctantly parked our bikes when we heard our final "it's going cold" from Mum, to say that dinner was ready.

Life can be like 'riding a bike' – we start off in childhood with the 'let's play' attitude, with our imagination as the road map, joy and freedom powering our feet on the 'pedals' and we're open to all and any possibilities. Soon real-life pressures take over, we naturally prioritise, we shift our focus and suddenly we find ourselves in the middle of our life, at the crossroads with our 'Second Act' begging us on stage.

I wrote this book to help you get out of your head and back into your heart where you'll reconnect with ideas, get creative, tap into, and uncover what brings you joy and excites you. There you'll find your path – signposted 'Your Purpose'.

'From Frightened to FABULOUS' could be the exact next 8 steps you need to reconnect or uncover the new and improved YOU with purpose and a life you desire and so deserve.

My road to achieve total wellness and a deeply fulfilling life, inside and out - has 8 pivotal parts.

Are You Ready to Design Your Second Act or Next Phase?

Here are your starting blocks and the foundation to your 'next phase' along with a gentle nudge from me:

- Be curious – look and you will find, you never know, it could take you down a path to your purpose
- Have courage to try – step out of your comfort zone – give it a go! don't let your BS (belief system) hold you back
- Recharge your desire to learn – stay engaged, stimulated and

Interested.

I am SO excited to share with you the 8 Secret Steps to look and feel FABULOUS on the inside AND outside.

It's time to celebrate the best version of you to 'feel good in the skin you're in'

You DESERVE a good life

It all starts on the INSIDE!

I want to help you unpack, rediscover and reconnect with how beautiful and brilliant you are. To recognize your skills, appreciate your experience and express your creativity.

You're going to make a list of all the things you love to do and are good at, then understand what's holding you back, decide what you want, then you'll design the steps to get there!

Oh, by the way, once you're feeling fabulous on the inside, you're going to refresh, update and feel FABULOUS on the outside too. Those who change their lives have one thing in common – **they take action**.

You're going to take those ideas, thoughts and dreams floating around inside your head and make them real by **taking action!**

It's time to LIVE YOUR DREAM

"It is confidence in our bodies, minds and spirits that allows us to keep looking for new adventures" – Oprah

Here are a few photos of people I met along the way!

From Rock Stars and Supermodels to Formula 1 Drivers and even a Prince...

Seal– *Musician and Singer*

Sting – *Musician and Singer*

Cindy Crawford - *Business Woman and Supermodel*

Tom Jones – *Musician and Singer*

Shirley Bassey - *Singer*

Yasmin Le Bon - *Business Woman and Supermodel*

Petra Nemcovà - *TV Host, Philanthropist and Supermodel* -

Terezà Maxova - *Supermodel*

HSH Prince Albert II of Monaco

HSH Prince Albert II of Monaco

HSH Prince Albert II of Monaco

Vitantonio Liuzzi - *Formula 1 Driver*

Adrian Sutil - *Formula 1 Driver -*

Jaime Alguersuari - *Formula 1 Driver*

Lucas Di Grassi - *Formula 1 Driver -*

Nico Rosberg - *Formula 1 Driver -*

Cora Schumacher - *Wife of Formula 1 Driver -*

Sir **Stelios Haji-Ioannou** - *Businessman, Founder of Easyjet -*

Dr. John Demartini - *Professional Speaker, Author and Business Consultant -*

Patty Aubery – Author, *President of The Jack Canfield Training Group (Chicken Soup for the Soul) leading consultant -*

Jack Canfield - *Author of the Best-Selling book, The Success Principles. Co-creator, #1 NYTimes Best-Selling Book Series, Chicken Soup for the Soul -*

James Malinchak - *Featured on the hit ABC TV Show* ***Secret Millionaire.*** *#1 Speaker, Marketing Coach and Consultant for 30-years -*

Kevin Eastman - *Assistant NBA Coach – Los Angeles Clippers, Assistant NBA Coach –Boston Celtics, Top Consultant for NIKE Basketball -*

Rudy Ruettiger - *The Inspiration Behind the Blockbuster Movie* ***"RUDY"*** *Named one of the All-Time Greatest Sports Movies. -*

Trinny Woodall - *Founder of Beauty Empire* ***"Trinny London"*** *Author and TV Presenter -*

TV Hosts: Ruth & Eamonn Holmes
'How the Other Half Lives'

RoadDog TV Productions – The French Property Show

Sky TV (Sky Living) 'Who'd be a Billionaire'

SECRET STEP ONE: LEARN TO LOVE YOU

Reconnect with your true self

Who are you today?

What are your personal qualities?

What is your story?

What are your core values?

What are your strengths?

When was the last time you openly 'blew your own trumpet' or shared your 'medals' and accomplishments with someone?

I have a client (let's call her Barbara), who somehow 'forgot' to tell me she was regional ladies golf champion – and oh, by the way, ran the London Marathon at 60 years old!

I was speechless to think these epic trophies were being brushed aside. Don't be a 'Barbara!' Speak up, share your brilliance! We naturally don't like to brag, and somewhere along the way our self-confidence has taken a backseat. Now it's time for you to be reminded of your brilliance. This isn't bragging; it's recognizing the best of yourself.

We all have things about ourselves that we want to change or improve, but real change begins when you can deeply appreciate all that you've been through with all the twists, turns and challenges you have faced. If you're constantly criticising and comparing yourself, you'll never feel good enough because your inner critic is relentless and self-deprecating – so tell her to take a hike!

Accept yourself just as you are even your 'not so good at' traits – after all, they are a part of you too.

It's important to stop, ask yourself questions and then have the patience, desire and ability to 'hear' the answers.

I know it can be scary to sit in silence, especially when we are so programmed for momentum and change. But the key is to press the 'pause' button.

As you move through the steps in this book, write your answers down, declare them on the pages of this book so you can see them, study them, and let them empower you.

To help you kick-start and step into the **BODY and LIFE** you desire, I'd like to offer you a gift ($497 Value) **go to: www.heidireboot.com** and enjoy my **5 x Full Body Workouts for Beginners** and a **14-day Healthy Eating Plan** to take you from feeling mediocre to **magnificent in 14-Days!**

By reconnecting with your authentic self, by finding the clarity and appreciating all that you are, and all that you've done, you'll tap into the self-compassion and self-love required to confidently move into the next phase of your life feeling empowered and enthusiastic.

Life is full of excitement and challenge. It's important to keep learning and uncovering things about yourself that are unexpected; to feel happy by just being you.

You might recall from earlier in the book, how in the midst of a family meltdown, I defiantly wrote a list of all I'd accomplished up to that moment, to show to my Dad. I had to do it because I felt he didn't know me. I felt underestimated, even though, of course, I knew that it was just that he was so worried. Well, after showing it to him, I kept that list. What's more, I still have it today. Now I just keep adding to it with pride!

This is the same list I want you to write: it's transformational!

"You either walk inside your story and own it, or you stand outside your story and hustle for your worthiness" – Brené Brown

I want you to unapologetically embrace the power of self-love and self-compassion, have a deep appreciation for who you are and your journey so far.

When you look in the mirror, see the things you like about the way you look instead of always focusing on the things you don't.

Fully understand that YOU hold the power to create your own dream life…now start to fully embrace it!

Take time now to reconnect with the real YOU.

- Do you feel energized and comfortable in a large group, or do you prefer your own company, quiet solitude and calm reflection?
- Are you curious, eager for knowledge and change, or do you prefer stability, consistency, and routine?
- Are you impulsive, does excitement and unpredictability challenge and motivate you, or do you find comfort in structure and organisation?
- When or what makes you feel most authentic?

These are important things to ask yourself because it's difficult to feel joy when your life and environment doesn't match and align with who you truly are.

Uncovering Your 'WHO'

Who are you? Write down 8 clarifying descriptions of 'who' you are (outside of friend and family relations. Don't include, for example, Mum, sister, friend etc.) Dig deep and don't rush.

I am a ___________ **I am a** ______________

I am a ___________ **I am a**_______________

I am a ___________ **I am a**_______________

I am a ___________ **I am a** ______________

Know who you are: Answer the following questions (write them down) to reunite with your true self.

What makes you happy and come alive?

- ____
- ____
- ____
- ____

Who do you want to fight for?

- ______________________________
- ______________________________
- ______________________________
- ______________________________

What would you regret not fully doing, being, or having in your life?

- ______________________________
- ______________________________
- ______________________________
- ______________________________

When or where do you feel most authentic?

- ______________________________
- ______________________________
- ______________________________
- ______________________________

Your Personal Qualities

What do you consider your 5 best personal qualities - the 5 things that your friends love about you, or come to you for?

1. ______________________________

2. ______________________________

3. ______________________________

4. ______________________________

5. ______________________________

Now you have locked in *who* you are, and your personal qualities, it's time to deeply connect with your personal story.

Pay attention to your life, appreciate the journey you've been on and know you are 100% responsible for your life path, listen to your inner voice.

You've done some amazing things so far, things that became easy for you. Now you need to believe in something new, more importantly you need to believe in YOU – believe in your potential – there's a reason why you're here.

What if everything you've been through, the challenges, the traumas, the joy, the peaks and the valleys, all that life experience has brought you to today and have moulded you into who you are now?

What if it was all for a reason?

What if you could truly love yourself with all your imperfections, strengths, weaknesses and all your quirkiness in between?

It's time to reconnect with all that you have accomplished, experienced and overcome that has brought you to today.

I want you to see, in print, who you truly are and what you've done in your life, you're going to appreciate the journey you've been on.

Think back and list what you've already achieved and then re-read and see how far you've come, knowing that this was all necessary to bring you to where you are today.

The clarity and reflection will give you the hints and whispers of what makes you happy and come alive.

Your Story So Far...

What is your story? Write down some key facts, accomplishments, challenges and adventures, big or small, that tell the story of your life…let it flow!

It's important that we value and cherish the challenges alongside the triumphs. Parts of your story so far, might have been challenging, disruptive and painful, but it's moulded you into who you are, and has brought with it all the knowledge, experience and strength you possess.

Those accomplishments need to be recognised; it's too easy to brush your brilliance under the carpet. Take stock of what you've done, look at the beauty of what you have created or uncovered.

Do you see how important it is to re-connect and remind yourself of what you have experienced, the patchwork of your life that sewn together, has brought you to today?

CELEBRATE my awesome friend! You are **BRILLIANT** just as you are, the best is yet to come!

"You have brains in your head.
You have feet in your shoes.
You can steer yourself in any direction you choose.
You're on your own.
And you know what you know.
You are the guy who'll decide where to go". – Dr Seuss

Your Core Values

What do you value? The things that are most important to you, the non-negotiables.

Please **circle your 10 core values** and, as best you can, put them in order of importance (1 being the most important) - feel free to add to this list

A list of Core Values

- Authenticity
- Achievement
- Adventure
- Authority
- Autonomy
- Balance
- Beauty
- Boldness
- Compassion
- Challenge
- Citizenship
- Community
- Competency
- Contribution
- Creativity
- Curiosity
- Determination
- Fairness
- Faith
- Fame
- Friendships
- Fun
- Growth
- Happiness
- Honesty
- Humour
- Influence
- Inner Harmony
- Justice
- Kindness
- Knowledge
- Leadership
- Learning
- Love
- Loyalty
- Meaningful Work
- Motivation
- Openness
- Optimism
- Peace

- **Pleasure**
- **Poise**
- **Passion**
- **Positivity**
- **Popularity**
- **Recognition**
- **Religion**
- **Romance**
- **Reputation**
- **Respect**
- **Responsibility**
- **Security**
- **Self-Respect**
- **Service**
- **Spirituality**
- **Stability**
- **Success**
- **Status**
- **Trustworthiness**
- **Wealth**
- **Wisdom**

What you value can change as you move through life.

Sometimes you need to stop and decide if what you value is relevant today.

Many of the women I have worked with, have eventually come to the realization that holding on to what was previously a core value like, for example, 'security' was keeping her trapped. As she progressed through life, 'security' was less important, giving way perhaps to 'curiosity' and 'adventure' – values more suited to the way she was now feeling or wanted to feel.

Are there any values you'd like to let go of and replace with new ones?

LET GO OF	REPLACE WITH
1. ____________	1.______________
2. _____________	2._________________
3. _______________	3._________________
4._________________	4._________________
5._______________	5.__________________

I want you to know you are perfect just as you are today.

Know Your Strengths

What are your strengths and passions? The things that you're good at, make you happy, and give meaning and purpose to your life?

You're probably thinking: "I don't know, never really thought about it."

Well, it's time for you to knuckle down and see it in print!

Often when I start working with a client, I realise they've disconnected from the things they love to do and are naturally good at – those are the things that they don't need to be asked to do, they lose track of time doing them, and would do them for free.

Your strengths are your innate talents, done without thinking. They come so easily to you; they're natural, and that's why they're a strength.

I want you to reconnect with what you're good at and love doing.

It's so much easier to complain about what you're NOT good at, but imagine how your life would be if you focused only on what you're BRILLIANT at!

It's time to reconnect with your unique talents, passions, and strengths, the ones you must share with the world.

The following questions will help trigger and remind you what they are.

What are you naturally good at and when you do this, you lose track of time? (a skill, ability, gift)

- ______________________________
- ______________________________
- ______________________________

What were your favourite things to do in the past?

- ______________________________
- ______________________________
- ______________________________

What do other people typically ask you for help with?

- ______________________________
- ______________________________
- ______________________________

If you had to teach something, what would it be?

- ______________________________
- ______________________________
- ______________________________

Your passions are not random, THEY ARE YOUR CALLING.

Your purpose can evolve but your talents, passions and strengths rarely change – they were given to you, but how you use them can change at different times in your life.

You've been given everything you need. It's all inside of you, and all you have to do is align those unique talents, passions and strengths, then share them with the world. Once you do, you'll uncover a life full of meaning, a life you desire and certainly deserve!

Strengths + Passions = Purpose

Now you've reconnected with 'who' you are, what you value and what you're good at. This creates a solid foundation, the clarity, and a starting point to design the roadmap.

You're in control of your future, no more excuses.

Once you know what you want, the choice is simple: either take action or don't.

The more important question is this: what happens if you don't? If not now, then when?

Is it going to be one day or Day One? It's your choice.

SECRET STEP TWO: WHAT'S HOLDING YOU BACK?

Your B.S.

Fear of Change

Comfort Zone

Forgiveness

Your 'not enough'

Fear of Greatness

Your B.S. (Belief System)

You get trapped in the framework of your beliefs.

You decide 'who' you are based on your beliefs about yourself.

Your values, rules, self-identity, negative and limiting beliefs can hold you back from reaching your goals and true self.

The beliefs that may have served you well at age 22 may no longer be fit for purpose at 42, 52, 62 or 72 years. It's about your Belief System (your B.S.) and how changing what you believe can change your life.

It's time to release beliefs and habitual thoughts, the patterns and stories you tell yourself that limit and hold you back so you can open the door to new opportunities for growth with joy and enthusiasm.

Let's start by releasing the negative beliefs and those habitual thoughts that define the current stories you're telling yourself.

- Is it time to reframe an event or something in the past?
- Is it time to let it go and stop thinking about how things should be?
- Is it time to see them how they are so that then you can release, forgive and move out of 'stuck'?

Know Your Limiting Beliefs

Let go of the stories, they are limiting you; release them so you can live authentically, feeling empowered and aligned with your core values and who you truly are.

Once you release your limiting beliefs you can identify your new desired beliefs - ones that will inspire and support your inner journey of self-discovery and transformation so you can immediately start showing up more powerfully and confidently.

You can decide to change any limiting belief and replace it with a new one; it just takes awareness, desire and practice.

LET GO OF	REPLACE WITH
• ____________	____________
• ____________	____________
• ____________	____________
• ____________	____________

Fear of Change

Like it or not, we are creatures of habit. We like our routine and don't like to be faced with uncertainty or the unknown.

In fact, our brains, through evolution, are just trying to keep us safe. We don't step off the curb into oncoming traffic, we don't drive on the wrong side of the road, the fear is there to protect us and keep us safe.

In most cases fear of change stops us from taking action alongside guilt, anxiety and self-doubt which in turn can stop us getting ahead in life.

By nurturing our self-esteem and self-confidence, we can choose to kick that stupid 'fear of change' to the curb!

Change is inevitable, so expect it to come, whether it's good or bad – it can cause stress… as Forrest Gump said, "You never know what you're gonna' get."

Let me ask you:

- Is the fear of making a change holding you back?
- Is the fear of the unknown debilitating?
- Is the fear of judgement from others limiting you?
- Are you afraid of letting go of the familiar, even though it isn't what you want?
- Do you hear yourself whispering 'yes' to any or all of the above?

That was me too!

I was stuck and too scared to change anything…

It took years before I realized that NOTHING would improve or change until I stopped to think, to reflect, to rediscover, and reconnect with myself. Only then could I begin the journey.

What this means for you is that you need to loosen your grip, be open, flexible, know that change happens when you're outside your comfort zone and, you know what? Everything doesn't always need to make sense right away.

- What fears are you habitually experiencing that are holding you back from having the life you desire?
- Is it time to recognize your limiting fears and face them, break them down to understand the origin?
- Is the fear real, or is it just an excuse?

What Do You Fear?

Write down your 3 most dominant fears today - What are you afraid of?

1 ____

2. ____

3. ____

Who/how would you be without those fears?

- ____
- ____
- ____

The reality is that there are four primal fears:

- The fear of losing someone's love or having your love rejected
- The fear of being helpless, so you don't feel safe (feeling vulnerable)
- The fear of losing control – control of yourself, control of others, control of what will happen, when or how it will happen.
- The fear of not being seen as valuable, necessary or worthy.

Remember we're all fearful of change on some level and uncertainty is inevitable no matter what, where or when, let's face it, that void straight ahead can be scary.

<u>Client Case #2:</u>

Susan's mother was diagnosed and died within 6 months. The shock and grief, like a tidal wave, came crashing down, leaving Susan (not her real name) drowning in sadness unable to find joy in any area of her life; she'd lost direction, enthusiasm for anything, she felt her life had come to a screeching halt.

Two years passed, then Susan reached out to me for help.

Susan's mother was French. She'd moved to America as a young woman, married and had one child. Susan's childhood was happy, raised mostly by her mother, as her father was away working and not around much. She grew up surrounded by French antiquities, music and food. Her mother told her stories of life in Paris, Susan loved those stories of another world, another life.

Now living in that very same house with her husband, surrounded by the very same ornaments, furniture and memorabilia that she'd inherited from her mother, it felt like a golden cage.

Her mother's death had left her with the weight of the past, an identity that wasn't hers, and the guilt and inability to move forward and make any kind of change.

Susan naturally found comfort in the memories, the cupboards full of French coffee cups, the wallpaper in her childhood bedroom, faded but still hanging, her mother's jewellery and signature French silk scarves in the wardrobe.

She needed help to find a way forward and out of the past, which she described as a dark room, the door of which she couldn't find nor even the light switch.

She'd spent the last two years feeling numb, trapped in her story, soothing her sadness with food and bottles of French wine. Her marriage felt empty, although not from her husband's lack of trying; he was doing his best to support her and keep life ticking over.

She was indifferent about her job, had disconnected from her friends, and rarely liked to leave the house except for the daily drive to work.

When I began coaching with Susan, the most obvious missing starting block was her lack of self-identity and her story.

She didn't know who she was.

She had a full life before her mother's death, and although she had accomplished many things, sadness and loss had left her with no self-belief or self-worth and a story she kept telling herself, and everyone else, about her mother's death.

Furthermore, she had no motivation, or desire, to show up in her own life.

I believe that self-acceptance and self-love can only be harnessed when you reconnect with the woman you've left behind or disassociated yourself from. Her mother's death became Susan's 'story' and this negative event was influencing her life.

The story she was telling herself had become her identity.

Susan had to acknowledge that her mother's death wasn't 'who' she was; it was what had happened to her. She had lost touch with the person she was before her mother died.

"Who am I without my mother's French style and savoir faire?" she said, "Who am I without the stories of my mother's childhood in Paris?"

In fact, those very stories had permeated into being HER childhood stories, so that Susan had adopted her mother's identity, and disconnected from her own.

Once we tapped into 'who' she really was, her talents and strengths, once we uncovered the woman she had left behind, the gates opened and we were ready to step across the line.

Now we could reconnect with the Susan before she lost her mother and we could identify and anchor the brilliance and talents that were in hiding.

We also tapped into the patterns and triggers that were causing her stress, guilt and self-doubt and created a new framework of beliefs and core values -- the things that Susan truly believed and valued, not the ones handed down by her mother.

Over a period of eight months working together, Susan was able to release the constant dark cloud of guilt overhead.

Then the obvious next step was the 'golden cage' as Susan called it, and how to reinvent the house to make it her own. She donated a lot of the china and furniture, although she kept the French coffee cups, and slowly, she and her husband began redecorating and redesigning the house their way.

With clarity came new goals and a dream to go to visit Paris, we were now creating the roadmap and stepping stones towards a 'new and improved' version of Susan.

Another major challenge for Susan was the weight she had gained, much of it from emotional eating. She knew her energy was low and somewhere along the way, she'd lost her 'sexy female'. She wanted to lose weight, tone and strengthen her body to feel healthier, confident and attractive again.

"Let's do it!" I said.

I designed a nutritious, balanced diet and a progressive and manageable exercise plan; she lost weight, increased her energy, improved her mindset, and soon became enthusiastic about the future.

Her mental state completely changed by simply improving her nutrition and adding regular exercise...bingo!

The truth is, our thoughts, feelings and beliefs can positively or negatively affect the health of our bodies. Also, what we eat and how we exercise can hugely impact our mental state.

This was hugely apparent when I was working with Susan.

With this newfound self-confidence she started interviewing for a new job, and so we worked on interview techniques, her professional image and personal style. We shopped for a new wardrobe that suited the woman she had become. She had dropped almost two dress sizes and naturally it boosted her self-confidence.

Another goal Susan set was to go to Paris to see where her mother was born and raised and to reconnect with her mother's memory there, in a positive and peaceful way. She was so enthusiastic that she signed up for evening classes at the local junior college to learn French, then she and her husband booked a 2-week holiday in Paris, which coincided with their 25th wedding anniversary.

Susan went from frightened to FABULOUS!

It's so incredibly powerful how your thoughts impact your emotions and they then create your life experience.

You can get stuck in the past or in a story that's trapping you from fully enjoying your life.

Maybe it's just the way you're thinking and it's preventing you from seeing things another way. What happens is you keep repeating this situation or thought process over and over again.

Only when you stop the 'storytelling' can you begin to release yourself from the past, and create new empowering beliefs that give you the confidence to move forward embracing new possibilities with a liberating sense of freedom.

Comfort Zone

Are you trapped in your comfort zone, are you hiding, and scared of change? Do you feel safe there because life is consistent and predictable? The flip side is there's no growth, no new experiences and limited joy.

When you stay in your comfort-zone you're just sticking to what you know, doing the same thing every day which keeps you safe, secure, and life is consistent, reliable and predictable.

- Where's the joy?
- Where's the discovery and learning?
- How will you know what you're capable of if you stay in your comfort zone?

You're blocking yourself from reaching your potential and from having new life experiences.

Doing something outside what feels comfortable and safe doesn't have to be an 'all or nothing' decision; you can take small, calculated steps.

Start by being curious; Go on an adventure, look for something that will challenge you, that pushes you, that might make you feel anxious but in a positive way.

A healthy level of anxiety can be welcomed and can motivate and direct you to try new things, create new opportunities. Even meeting new people, joining a gym, an art class, book club, tennis group, are manageable ways to step out of your comfort zone. In fact, just making a new friend takes you out of your comfort zone.

The truth is, you need a certain amount of anxiety to stay engaged, stimulated, and perhaps even to spark change. When you're existing on automatic pilot, you can find yourself feeling flat, bored, and lethargic about everything. Some people create drama or friction in their life just to feel significant.

Avoiding anxiety will hold you back.

Take a risk – what's the worst that could happen? It doesn't have to initiate fear and dread, but when you take a risk, you open the door for growth.

But let's remember, we're not all made the same. The flip side to 'take a risk' or 'spread your wings' could be 'ignorance is bliss;' the not knowing what you're missing suits many, and not everyone is a risk-taker as risk is subjective.

Fear of the unknown keeps us 'safe' and carries us through life.

I remember sitting with my Grandma on her 100th birthday, she was holding the letter she had received from the Queen acknowledging her massive milestone. I wanted to know more about my lovely, kind Grandma who, along with my Grandad, made meat and potato pie every Wednesday for me and my sister after school. I wanted to find out how this fun-loving lady, who let us play 'shop' in her food pantry and pirate ships on her dining table, had lived her precious 100 years.

And so, I asked her. Her reply is engraved on my heart: "I have no exciting stories to tell you" she whispered, "I only wish I had done more, seen more, lived a more exciting life, I had a very plain, ordinary life."

Then she squeezed my hand, smiled and looked at me with her kind eyes and I knew instantly that her words, her touch, her smile, were in fact her signal to me to live, love and shine bright in my life, to truly strive for a full life and avoid 'plain and ordinary'.

All I can say is "Thank-you Grandma. You passed me the baton, I'm in my lane, and I'm running my race!"

Curiosity, wanderlust and adventure have fuelled my life since I was 16, as you have read in the first half of my book. My childhood was wonderful and gave me such a solid, balanced foundation, and once I'd experienced, seen and discovered what was 'out there' I couldn't unsee it.

I'm here to tell you that an average life is not an option.

Once you've made the decision to make a change, look forward and don't look back. What was, is over; what's now is what matters and the possibilities for living a happier, more purposeful and positive life is in your hands.

Forgiveness

We can all struggle with forgiveness. It's challenging to forgive and release anger, disappointment or sadness due to someone else's actions. By forgiving that person, it somehow makes us feel we have lost. We believe that when we 'hold our ground' and don't forgive, it validates our position and we win.

The truth: You can free yourself from the past through forgiveness.

You can let go of any resentment, bitterness and grudges, you still carry, by forgiving that person, it doesn't mean forgetting or excusing the behaviour, hurt or disappointment but it will free you from the ‘control’ this person has over you

You need to ask yourself what this resentment and anger you’re choosing to hold on to is giving you? How is it serving you? Is it giving you the ability to play the ‘victim card’?

This might be completely valid in your mind but it’s not helping or serving you. It’s hard work to live with that negative energy and it limits your ability to be happy and free.

What you’ll finally realise is: the person you can’t forgive is on holiday in the Bahamas, drinking piña coladas, they don’t care and you’re the only one feeling angry, sad, and disappointed. So, who’s suffering?

Forgiveness is your choice -- take back your power!

Forgive yourself and choose to forgive the person who hurt you, even if they don’t deserve it; understand forgiveness is a process, followed by compassion that you can adjust over time.

You can’t change the other person or their behaviour – forgiveness is ALL about you and your ability to choose how you think and the emotions you feel. Forgiveness is how it can change YOUR life and bring YOU peace, along with healing, creating healthier relationships and reducing stress and anxiety.

“Forgiveness is the attribute of the strong” – Mahatma Gandhi

Self-doubt, ‘Not enough’, Fear of Greatness

That self-doubt is just negative self-talk. It stops you from taking risks, it’s your protection from failure. Let’s be honest, we all know about the fear of failure and how it often holds us back from taking action. If you do try something and it doesn't work, you can easily go back to what you know because 'at least you tried' and it feels comfortable and straightforward. Whereas success will mean change, which can be scary and difficult for some people even if they think that's what they want.

Fear of greatness is self-doubt in disguise.

Don't let that inner critic take charge and hold you back from success. That voice inside of you that's always telling you that you should do it differently or you've got it wrong. Feeling not good enough will get you nowhere. You must put fear in its place and know how unique and special you are! You need to remember you're a work in progress. You aren't going to magically wake up one morning and say, "YUP! I've got this!"

You just need to move forward, take a step and have faith – just having faith makes you appreciate that there is doubt and uncertainty. Trust yourself, trust your abilities, trust you can do it and that you'll figure it out.

When you think you might be criticised, self-doubt kicks in to keep you from taking action.

We all know that we can't get rid of our fears, they just need to be managed, so… enter courage! Courage is recognizing the fear, having belief in yourself, and taking action anyway.

I remember when I wanted to divorce, I had to dig really deep for the courage to move forward. I was haunted every night by self-doubt, fear and 'what if'. Be kind to yourself – tell yourself you CAN do this and you DO belong.

Know that success is progressive and the knowledge you gain through DOING will make you feel competent, which will release the fear and feed your confidence!

To be self-confident is to trust in your own abilities and know-how, self-confidence is like a muscle you need to consistently work on, for it to grow.

Believe that you can do what you set your mind to and for those who think your age might be holding you back, remember - **you're never too old and it's never too late!**

Imagine what your life would look like with the success you're aiming for, once you have a framework and a goal, just power forward, knowing fear will always be present, but do it anyway and expect success.

Here are 4 things to remember on your journey towards success:

- You are unique, don't compare yourself to others
- Take responsibility for your own happiness
- Have supportive and kind thoughts of yourself
- Develop an attitude of gratitude, you will feel happier and more positive.

This takes courage and time, but only YOU can make it happen.

"Talk to yourself like you would to someone you love" -Brené Brown

Client Case #3:

My client Christine (not her real name) decided she wanted to become a lawyer at the age of 50. After spending 20 years at home raising a family, she contacted me to be her co-pilot and coach to help reach her goal.

She was battling with self-doubt internally, and negativity from the people closest to her. Although her goal was high, her self-confidence was low.

We began by reconnecting with her inner, brilliant self, the academic she had put aside to raise her children. We then began working on eliminating the obstacles she had created in her mind...they were; fear of judgement, fear of failure, and 'it's too late'.

The other, less obvious fears she had were 'what happens if I'm successful?' and 'how will this affect the people in my life?'

I coached Christine on all her limiting beliefs and we were able to find clarity, and a manageable and comfortable way forward. Her enthusiasm for change empowered her and she felt excited as we began designing the roadmap to the goal.

We worked together for twelve months and today she works as a lawyer in London and has created a stunning 'Second Act' that includes her new identity, her close family, and her independence alongside.

You need a certain amount of self-belief to feel confident, but having self-belief alone doesn't mean you're loaded with self-confidence.

I think self-belief is the easier of the two; self-confidence is the challenging one, especially when you haven't been 'in the game' for a while, due to various reasons. You give your attention and focus to everyone else, hiding behind their successes and forget to check in with your own ideas, plans and dreams.

You need to just start before you feel ready because if you wait for things to be 'perfect' you'll never do it. Yes, you might make mistakes at first, but as you grow more competent you grow more confident!

Need to Please

So many of us have the 'need to please' and it's a valid feeling, it's a good thing and creates an amicable existence for us all but, the challenge begins with consistent self-sacrifice when we dismiss our own feelings and desires to please those around us. We want to be liked, we try to please others and we give too much importance to other people's opinions.

We look outside ourselves for validation and appreciation. It's time to tap into what YOU want, your true DESIRES. Remember…other people's opinion of you is none of your business.

Know what you want, know your path and just DO IT - persistently, consistently and with a generous spirit!

To help you kick-start and step into the **BODY and LIFE** you desire, I'd like to offer you a gift - go to: www.heidireboot.com and enjoy my **5 x Full Body Workouts for Beginners** and a **14-day Healthy Eating Plan** to get you feeling energised and strong as you go through this book.

SECRET STEP THREE: UNLEASH YOUR DESIRES

What do you want?

How do you want to feel?

You've reconnected with who you are and what's holding you back and now you need to decide what you want in this next phase of your life.

It's time to explore your desires and where you want to go!

Sounds easy right? On the one hand you realise there's SO much to do, you're only halfway so crack on and make it happen but then, on the other hand, it's not always clear what your heart desires.

Are you settling for less than you want? What's the dream?

Remember, self-love is not selfish.

It's a given that we all want freedom, to feel happy, content, with a sense of peace and wellbeing – the question is "What will it take for you to feel that happiness, that freedom and peace?"

It can sometimes be helpful to reflect back to a time when you felt free, happy, content and peaceful. Think about what was going on in your life then. What were you doing or not doing? Bring those elements to your present life today.

It can be challenging to actually voice what you want. No one has ever asked you and more importantly you've never asked yourself. The question was easier to answer when you were in your twenties and even thirties…perhaps you were on a career path, building your own business or starting a family.

Once you have a career under your belt, your children are grown and independent and you're only 'halfway' in life, it's more challenging to commit to a new goal or even decide on one.

What I want you to know is this: you are fully loaded, you've got oodles of life-experience, knowledge, know-how and opportunity ahead of you.

Client case #4

My client *Sandra (not her real name) was 60. "That horrible age" she said - she could manage 50 but 60! She'd been divorced over 20 years and her 2 children lived abroad. She was on her own and had been working in the same job for 25 years, heading towards retirement. She felt lonely. "Every week's the same, I'm always on my own" she said. "I've got lovely friends but I just want that special someone...is it too late for me?"*

She said she felt invisible, old-fashioned and unattractive. "Retirement is pulling me to the edge" she said, "it's asking me to jump, but I don't want to, I'm not ready, it makes me feel old."

She knew she had a habit of dwelling on past mistakes and what could have been. She also had a nagging fear of becoming ill and having no one around to help her. Unfortunately, this didn't stop her eating all the wrong food, knowing it was unhealthy and hurting her body. Food was her comfort and the constant and dependable way to feel 'better' although the frustration and self-hatred she felt minutes after, was overwhelming. Sandra was overweight and was on a rollercoaster of emotional eating, she lacked self-confidence, self-worth but felt totally unmotivated to look after her body and health...why bother!

Sandra contacted me. She needed help to unpack her fears and self-doubt. It was clear that she needed nutrition and exercise advice along with accountability to follow through. Ultimately, Sandra was asking for help to reconnect with the woman she knew was hidden inside, the fun, social, sexy woman who wanted to feel healthy, energetic, young and attractive again. She wanted to share her life with someone, to start dating and find love again, but needed to build back the courage, self-confidence and trust in herself. She wanted to let go of the fear and self-doubt and create a vision and the stepping stones towards the next phase of her life.

We began with weekly life-coaching, nutrition and exercise sessions. As her diet improved, so did her mood and her enthusiasm to exercise. She felt more positive and in control of her life, no longer trapped in a rut. She lost weight, her skin brightened, her hair and nails improved and the vibrancy came back into her life...next step beauty and personal style.

I guided her on her hair, skin and make-up with tips and techniques along with my favourite product list. Then, we decluttered and reorganised her wardrobe. We had lots of fun shopping for missing items. Sandra's confidence skyrocketed. Her new wardrobe had to complement and show off her personality and the fabulous woman she had unleashed!

The final frontier for Sandra was dating. She wanted to find love again. We worked together on her profile and photos for a dating site and then, with some encouragement, she went out on a date. The great news is that Sandra met Philip six months later and they moved in together after a year of dating each other.

Get back in the driver's seat of your life, grab that steering wheel and take control of your future! Wave goodbye to regret, self-doubt and fears and HELLO to a life you love!

It's time for you to deeply connect with what you truly want. Identify and begin to nurture the things that light you up, so you can create a new vision for your life. Try something new, you might stumble upon a new passion.

Once you've decided on a goal for yourself, it needs to be specific and clear, with a timeline e.g. "I want to lose 10lbs in 12 weeks" or "Write my business plan in the next 60 days" or "Learn to waltz, so I can dance at my daughter's wedding in 6 months".

Start by opening your heart and mind, be curious, push your boundaries and think outside the box; this is your moment!

<u>What would you do if you knew you couldn't fail?</u>

Imagine that! A blank canvas, an open road…what do you dream of doing, accomplishing or experiencing?

Write down a minimum of 7 things and remember, for this exercise you can't fail at whatever it is you choose. Dream big!

You know what? Just to inspire you, I'll go first! Here's my list, and I fully expect you to share yours!

1. Sing like a rock star in front of thousands of people.

2. Be the leading lady in a romantic comedy.

3. Be a foster parent.

4. Fly a plane.

5. Build a school in Africa to educate young girls.

6. Enter an Ironman Triathlon.

7. Drive a fast car on a racetrack to win.

I know what you're thinking, NO CHANCE, Heidi!

Well, you're probably right, but it's important for you to remember that when you have a goal, a dream, or something you want to change, there's ALWAYS more than one way, one choice, one direction to take if you want to change your current situation.

Now it's your turn!

What's on YOUR list?

1. ______________________________

2. ______________________________

3. ______________________________

4. ______________________________

5. ______________________________

6. ______________________________

7. ______________________________

The truth is, there's always another option.

Often it takes some brainstorming and then the 'stepping stones' forward, but rarely are you ever without choice.

It always starts with mindset.

Don't listen to the constant jibber of your 'inner critic' that voice in your head that often torments you into staying put!

Beware of the enemy, SELF-DOUBT, who sheepishly creeps in and sits on your shoulder looking for approval and validation while whispering negativity into your ear. If you want to change, or improve yourself, your life, or start scratching things off your 'bucket list', or just find some inner peace, you're going to have to step out of your comfort zone and commit to something new, the unknown, a Second Act perhaps?

OPPORTUNITY is exciting because there's always a chance for GREATNESS!

You just need to decide what you want right now, today, tomorrow, next month, this time next year. Don't think about what you might lose, there's always compromise in any decision-making. No one wants to live with regret of what could have been if only you'd been able to just take that first step forward.

It's time to unlock what you desire in each area of your life, giving you the blueprint and roadmap towards the joy and purpose you're seeking. Once you decide what you want, along with the clarity about how you want to feel, it will give you the confidence to take action.

Here are 10 ideas to get you started;

1. **Have you been neglecting your health?** Now is the perfect time to focus on healthy eating, a new exercise routine, or getting back

on track with the one you might have left behind. Start walking or running, do strength training or Pilates. Listening to interesting podcasts when you power walk in the park or to your favourite audiobook will keep you going back for more.

2. **Turn your passion or hobby into a business.** What you love to do and are good at needs to be shared.
3. **Take 15 - 20 mins each morning to meditate.** Besides centring and calming you, it has other health benefits such as increased brain function, strengthens your immune system by releasing antibodies, improves memory and **you sleep better.**
4. **Plan an exciting trip.** Somewhere you've always dreamed of. Research the area and create the 'to-do' list for when you get there.
5. **Step-up your beauty routine.** Have a make-over, re-invent or update your image, buy new make-up, try a new hairstyle and colour.
6. **Get creative.** Write that book you know is inside of you, paint, sing, tap dance, join groups or sign up for classes – keep learning.
7. **Make new friends.** Choose opportunities to socialise through meet-ups, workshops, clubs or the gym.
8. **Up-date your wardrobe.** Is it time to re-think your image or style? Do you need those '10 key items' hanging in your wardrobe?
9. **Go back to work or volunteer.** Contribution and community are important for our mental and emotional health, being needed and valued are powerful emotions.
10. **Hire a Life-Coach.** She will help you tap into what makes you tick, what you need to feel engaged in life and keep you moving forward; she will help you identify what motivates and excites you and then

lead you gently down the path. No sitting at the crossroads ladies…the light is green!

Time to declare your goals and why. You're going to feel aligned by all the reasons WHY your dream means so much to you. The WHY is the feeling you want to feel. When you attach a feeling or emotion to a goal, it creates a deeper connection that's more than physical.

Write down what your life would look like if it were exactly as you wanted in each of the following areas of your life? Then alongside, write the word/s that best describe how you want to FEEL if it were exactly as you wanted? e.g: imagine you have a strong, healthy body, a wonderful nurturing relationship, the success in your job etc. how would it make you feel?

Exactly as I would like	**I would feel**
Health & Fitness	
Personal/ Growth	
Friends/Family	
Significant Other	
Possessions/Financial	
Home Environment	

Contribution

Career

Fun/Leisure

SECRET STEP FOUR: LEAN IN TO YOUR NEW ADVENTURE

Time to Take Action

Now you know what you want in each area of your life AND how you want to feel. You've taken back control, you're in the driver's seat with both hands on the steering wheel. You've stopped looking outwards for validation and you're ready to take action.

You have inner confidence along with the understanding of letting go, trusting yourself and the way forward. It's true, the unknown can be frightening, it can be difficult to let go of the familiar. Not anymore! You're fully loaded and ready for your new adventure.

What you focus on is your superpower. It's all about where you put your focus; this creates the direction of your life.

Focus on what you want, not on what you DON'T want!

Your unconscious mind has this strange way of directing your thoughts, so beware.

Client Case #5:

"Your scan shows cancer in both breasts" - the words that changed the direction of Jennifer's (not her real name) life. The horror, the fear, the shock...and then "am I going to die?"

She was advised to have a double mastectomy and then weeks of treatment and recovery sitting in numbness and a medicated fog, the battle began to reconstruct her breasts and her life.

She couldn't do it on her own, she had lost both parents several years ago and her sister lived on the other side of the world. Furthermore, she was depressed, frightened and totally shell shocked.

She was at a life-crossroads and needed help; that's when Jennifer and I connected.

It was very clear, as I began working with Jennifer, that she had totally shut down and disconnected from herself, her being. She immediately told me that she wasn't the same woman, that woman had gone, she felt let down by 'that woman' – she'd always lived a healthy, active life, always very conscious of good nutrition, she rarely drank alcohol, never smoked and now her body had let her down. Her mother had died of breast cancer so she was very aware of living a clean and healthy lifestyle.

She felt detached from her body and from the life she had before cancer.

Jennifer began her transformation by deeply appreciating all that she had been through, all the trauma, challenges and ultimately recognizing her inner strength.

She recovered physically, quite quickly, her body was strong, she was mentally strong and since her mastectomy, totally healthy. Naturally she was grateful to even be alive, luckily the cancer was caught early and after having both breasts removed, she had reconstructive surgery and to the outside world, she was on the right road and the healing would just take time, but... Jennifer regularly found herself sobbing uncontrollably in the shower with the warm water streaming down her body, a body she didn't recognize; the anxiety, sadness and fear was consuming her.

Together we began looking at the power of focus.

Jennifer was focusing on what she'd lost and what was missing, she missed the pre-cancer version of Jennifer and that body. She was very anxious about what other people would think, what about if she started dating, and how she could become intimate again. She kept comparing her now healthy, cancer free body to the way her body looked before the cancer. As we worked together over several weeks, she began to change her focus, she began to believe that her life was worth living, she was still beautiful and desirable and that she was, in fact, very grateful for what she'd gained, she had uncovered an overwhelming love and respect for her body.

She tapped into a stronger version of herself with new self-belief and trust... she now trusted herself - no matter what life threw at her, she knew that she would overcome, thrive and climb back in the ring to throw another punch.

Jennifer's life was threatened and it jolted her world and foundation, it triggered the desire for change, new meaning and purpose. She began to appreciate the 'second chance', the true gift she'd received; Jennifer was at a crossroads; it was time to open the door to new opportunities with joy and enthusiasm. She had found self-compassion and self-acceptance with a deep appreciation for her journey so far, now she was ready to create the next chapter of her life.

She decided to leave her job and set up a non-profit organization and now works with cancer hospitals helping others deal with the similar challenges.

We stepped up her nutrition to continue the repair of her body post-op and she was soon back to running and gym workouts. One evening at the gym she met David in the bar and now they're dating. During one of our coaching sessions, she told me that she felt confident and very sexy with her new breasts and David loved them too. Jennifer was able to reconnect with her true feelings, value and respect her body and from such a dark, scary place she has found her life purpose.

Let me ask you;

What are you focusing on?

- Do you focus on what you have, or what's missing?
- Do you focus on what you can control, or what you can't?
- Do you focus on the past, present, or future?

You're in control of your future, so stay focused on your dreams and goals and the stepping stones to reach them.

What and where you put your focus creates your reality.

<u>Client Case #6:</u>

Her abortion was scheduled for 9.30am that Wednesday morning. Cassi (name changed) had spent a sleepless night sweating, panicking, fraught with indecision...back and forth. She was 44, no children, an established lawyer, big salary, John, her new partner who she'd met just 8 months ago, worked in finance. She had a fabulous apartment and an equally fabulous life. Now, on this Wednesday morning, she was driving herself to the clinic not knowing how she truly felt about becoming a mother, she had decided not to tell John. Did she want to be a mother...now!? Would she get another chance, or was this it? She had to admit that having children was definitely on her 'to-do' list, but time passes so quickly, Cassi was always in control with everything scheduled...except having a baby.

She parked the car and sat with her head on the steering wheel, sobbing. She couldn't do it she couldn't go through with the abortion. The decision to keep the baby would change everything in her life, although she had no real concept of what that truly meant.

Fast-forward 18-months, Cassi contacted me in shreds.

"What happened to me?" she said, "Look at me, I used to be a hotshot lawyer and now I don't even recognize myself...or my life" she said sheepishly.

"Look at my skin, my hair, my body, I have no clothes that fit and I can't even find a reason to get out of my scruffy sweatpants every day, I feel trapped and useless" she told me "I love my baby, but I don't even feel as though I'm a very good mother"

I began coaching with Cassi. She needed to shift her focus and take on her new identity. By comparing herself to the 'other' woman, the hotshot lawyer she once was, she couldn't enjoy and feel confident as the natural, authentic mother she had become.

I helped her see that feeling trapped was her own mind creating boundaries. We designed a schedule for her, and for the baby, that included Cassi getting out of the house to meet other Mums and to find her 'tribe.'

Within a few weeks, she had joined some mother/baby groups and soon had a full schedule of activities with her baby and a wonderful group of Mums.

She just needed self-belief and reassurance – she learned to embrace motherhood and the empowered woman she had become. Once she dipped back into her natural talents, skills and strengths and redirected them into her present life, she was happy.

There were major improvements when she found a wonderful nanny to help her…this gave Cassi time for some self-care. In her professional life she had always prioritised exercise, and a healthy diet, which was important to her, but since having a baby, she'd pushed that aside.

We discussed healthy nutrition, exercise, and when to schedule time at the gym. We also went shopping to fill the gaps in her wardrobe – she didn't need her business suits right now so instead, we went shopping for soft, casual knits to feel comfortable, yet chic – a version of the woman she was keen to reconnect with.

We discussed her hairstyle and colour, then went to the hair salon together. Cassi loved her new colour and cut that was versatile, manageable and modern.

I introduced her to fabulous skincare and make-up – she complained she hadn't worn make-up in months, no time and she confessed she didn't feel attractive – this was a big breakthrough for her once we had her beauty regime in place.

Cassi, over a period of 6 months, tapped back into her confident female, she focused on motherhood, she let go of the woman she was and uncovered the woman she wanted to be by embracing new possibilities.

We can decide what to focus on, it's our choice.

Time to CELEBRATE and feel proud of yourself, look back, see how brilliant, talented and capable you are – embrace all that you've done, you are fully loaded, feel proud of yourself. You're AMAZING!

Don't ever underestimate yourself.

It's time to take ACTION and begin the journey towards living an amazing, joyful life.

You're going to decide on clear action steps towards the **'HOW'** you're going to achieve your newfound goals and then create the stepping stones and roadmap to get there, knowing that anything is possible for you.

You wrote down, in Secret Step Three, how your life would look and **FEEL** if it was exactly as you wanted in each area of your life. Refer back to that list and **copy** that same word/s into each area of life on the next page. Then go ahead and finish the sentence 'Then I will…' for each of the following areas. It's time to commit to an action, **one small (or big) for the next 30 days** to get you closer to where you want to be.

Health & Fitness.	**Action step/s**
If I want to FEEL______________	then I will________________
Personal/ Growth	**Action step/s**
If I want to FEEL______________	then I will________________
Friends/Family	**Action step/s**
If I want to FEEL______________	then I will________________
Significant Other	**Action step/s**
If I want to FEEL______________	then I will________________
Possessions/Financial	**Action step/s**
If I want to FEEL______________	then I will________________
Home Environment	**Action step/s**
If I want to FEEL______________	then I will________________
Contribution/Charity	**Action step/s**
If I want to FEEL______________	then I will________________

Career	**Action step/s**
If I want to FEEL_______________	then I will__________________
Fun/Leisure	**Action step/s**
If I want to FEEL_______________	then I will__________________

Now you're going to get clear on the timing of **WHEN** you will reach your goals. This will give you structure and motivation and make it much more likely they will happen.

Remember, nothing happens until you take that first step.

This is your First Year's Action Plan!

Go ahead and list what you will have achieved in 12 months from now. You know that every step you take is a step closer to your goal. As you move forward, write your goal/s down and stick them all over your house, office, even in your car. Tell those people you know, who will support you, as you move towards your goal, they can hold you accountable or even join you.

What I will have achieved by (write the **date here** 1 year from now)

- I will ____
- I will ____
- I will ____
- I will ____
- I will ____

What's the first step I need to take in the next…

48hrs ____

1 week ____

1 month ____

3 months ____

6 months ____

1 year ____

Imagine that you've achieved everything you set your mind to. You've created the life you dreamed of.

You've stepped into your power and confidently created the foundation for your 'next life-phase'.

- What would you say to yourself?
- Are you proud?
- Was it worth the effort and pushing through your fears?

Write as though you have created and accomplished everything you have ever wanted.

Manifest what you want by acting as if it's already here by writing a letter to yourself dated a year from today.

Dear____________________________

____

____

____

____

____

____

____

____

Love___________________________

You're halfway…WELL DONE!

You've completed the first **4 pivotal parts** to unlocking the best, most vibrant version of YOU! You took a deep dive into who you are, what's holding you back, what you want and the action steps to move you towards the life you desire.

Your inward journey of self-discovery has reminded you of how amazing you really are – and as Glinda, the Good Witch said, "You had the power all along, my dear!"

Now you're feeling good on the INSIDE, let's match it with feeling good on the OUTSIDE.

HEALTH & WELLNESS: LOOK GOOD FEEL GREAT

Step into the body and life you desire.

It's time to focus on nurturing your body with a nutritious diet.

Your thoughts, feelings and beliefs can positively or negatively impact the health of your body. What's also true is that what you eat and how much you exercise can directly impact your mental state. There's a direct and powerful relationship between your mind and body!

Hands up, who's ready to feel their healthiest yet?

SECRET STEP FIVE: NOURISH YOUR BODY

Living Healthier is Living Happier!

Nourishing your body is all about eating nutritionally dense food every-day. Being healthy isn't just about being disease-free, it's about living a vibrant, active life doing all the things you love.

Every level of your health is impacted by what you eat. You eat to build muscle, build healthy bones, gain energy, balance your hormones, boost your immune system, fix your gut and improve your heart health. Remember the impact of your food choices; every single bite of food you eat provides the raw materials for creating a vibrant, healthy body and long life.

Your physical health and wellness need to be a priority, and the quality of the food you eat is essential to living with good health.

"Food is medicine" - Dr Mark Hyman

I advise my clients to eat a clean, plant rich, nutrient dense, wholefood diet. Plant foods contain two unique ingredients: fibre and phytonutrients that optimize your gut microbiome and keep every system of your body functioning properly. The quality of the food you eat is directly related to the quality of the cells that make up every part of your body.

Healthy cells make healthy tissue that make healthy organs that make healthy systems = A Healthy Body.

Food isn't just about calories -- it's actually information for your

body.

Food is the fastest acting and most powerful medicine you can take to improve your health and change your life. Food controls your hormones, your brain chemistry, your immune system, your gut health and your structural system. **You ARE what you eat!**

Your DNA might be passed on through your parents, but you have control over how those genes are expressed and the biggest factor controlling your genes is what you eat. The food you eat sends messages to your genes telling them what to do. They create health or they create disease.

Eating a poor, unhealthy diet is directly linked to many preventable diseases like Type 2 diabetes, cancer and heart disease. Eating a wholefood diet, rich in colourful, phytochemical dense plants with clean protein, plenty of fibre, and healthy fats can prevent, treat and even reverse many chronic diseases.

What it's NOT about is restrictive diets that limit calories, leaving you nutrient deficient, feeling 'hangry' and ultimately are just a short-term fix.

Low-calorie diets fail for several reasons. Firstly, when you dramatically reduce the calories you eat, your body responds by releasing the hunger hormone ghrelin, so now you're feeling hungry and you're fighting a constant battle to resist any kind of food. A calorie restricted, crash diet might provide you with quick results, but it's not sustainable and it also affects your relationship with food, now you're emotionally caught up in the battle to resist eating.

When you stop the 'diet' there's a tendency to overeat – the deprivation affects you emotionally, physically and mentally – your brain and your body go into survival mode, your metabolism slows down, your body holds onto fat stores thinking there might be another period of starvation around the corner, and the yo-yo diet effect kicks in, now you're on the rollercoaster!

It's important to commit to upgrading the quality of the food you eat long term.

It's a conscious, lifestyle change forever!

Without good health, any dream or goal is superfluous.

Look at your daily habits and triggers that could be influencing your present eating patterns – how about that daily Starbucks habit – does it include a mid-morning snack? How about that end-of-the-day trigger at 'wine 'o clock' – is it accompanied by chips, peanuts or some other salty snack?

Release any unconscious habits that are sabotaging your goals to eat healthfully and replace them with ones that focus on healthy nutrition.

Release the habit of	**Replace with**
• ____________________	____________________
• ____________________	____________________
• ____________________	____________________

So many people spend years, or sometimes decades, suffering from chronic diseases of aging. Diabetes, Alzheimer's, cancer and heart disease are the big four. The risk of developing these diseases can be dramatically reduced by incorporating four simple behaviours: not smoking, regular exercise (minimum of three and a half hours per week), eating a healthy diet and maintaining a healthy weight.

The biggest cause of most age-related illnesses is insulin resistance. This is caused by eating too much starch (flour, pasta, potatoes, rice, bread, and refined grains) and sugars, in any form.

When you eat this addictive type of food, your pancreas has to pump out insulin into your blood to trigger the cells to 'open up and let the sugar in' so it can be used in the form of glucose for energy.

What happens when you constantly eat sugar and starchy foods the cells 'close shop' because they are saturated and can't take in any more sugar, so the sugar and insulin stay in your blood and is then stored as belly fat.

This belly fat creates inflammation in your body, alongside muscle loss and hormonal imbalance. Inflammation causes disease – the most common is Type 2 diabetes.

The GOOD news is that you can avoid and even reverse this suffering with a healthy diet. You should cut out, or radically reduce:

- **Starch** (bread, pasta, beans, white rice, including starchy veg like potatoes – replace with sweet potatoes)
- **Sugar** (cakes, cookies, baked goods and most fruit – eat berries, kiwis and pomegranate they are lower in sugar)

- **Processed foods.**

Eat a plant rich diet, clean protein and more 'good' fats and Omega-3 essential fatty acids (**avocado, salmon, sardines, mackerel, anchovies, nuts, seeds, olive oil**) so your body becomes insulin sensitive.

Then, after a few months, you can reintroduce small amounts of starchy vegetables, fruits and beans.

You're going to feel healthier, fitter, energised, vibrant, you'll have less brain fog and sleep better – all-round more alive!

Here are the 6 Pillars to live a long, healthy life!

- **A healthy diet**. Plant-rich, healthy fats, protein (animal and plant) and colourful vegetables (eat the rainbow), low sugar, low dairy.
- **Physical activity.** Daily activity of 30-minutes minimum (add resistance workouts with weights or bands for bone health, strength and maintaining metabolism)
- **Sleep**. Seven to nine hours
- **Manage stress**. Meditate, yoga, enjoy having a dog/pet
- **Social interaction**. Enjoy community, friendships and regular social connection
- **Mental fitness**. Reading, crosswords, board games.

My Nutrition 'bible' is **The Pegan Diet by Dr Mark Hyman**. He's a brilliant Functional Medicine Doctor and author of several New York Times Bestsellers, he also has a fantastic podcast called **'The Doctor's Farmacy'** – it's brilliant!

Ninety percent of the time, these are his (and my) diet rules, leaving the remaining ten percent to indulge and have treats! Life needs to be celebrated, social and family events are important and enjoyable so have some birthday cake and champagne – eating a healthy nutrient rich diet allows for some sneaky treats now and then!

I recommend:

- A plant-rich diet with plenty of dark leafy greens, a salad a day for sure (iceberg lettuce doesn't count) plus 7-9 servings of vegetables (75% of your plate needs to be colourful veg)
- Pasture-raised or organic chicken, turkey, and eggs
- Vegan protein like tempeh, tofu, lentils
- Wild fish or fish farmed with sustainable or regenerative practices such as low-toxin salmon, sardines, herring, mackerel (no tuna and swordfish)
- Low dairy – use milk alternatives like almond, rice, coconut, oat or soy instead
- Plenty of healthy fats including olive oil, avocado, nuts and seeds plus sardines, mackerel, salmon and anchovies for Omega-6 and 3 essential fatty acids (grab a handful of nuts as a snack - walnuts, Brazil, almonds, pecans or pistachios)
- Whole kernel grains/seeds like black rice, quinoa, amaranth, buckwheat
- Non-starchy beans and legumes including black-eyed beans, lentils, peas or mange-tout (avoid the starchier beans like kidney, lima and baked beans)
- NO white foods including white bread, flour, potatoes, rice, pasta, pastries, instead substitute with pumpernickel (dark, dense,

complex seeded bread)

- Low sugar/no added sugar
- NO processed food as they're all high in sugar, salt and trans-fat.
- Focus on disease fighting foods like leafy vegetables, polyphenol-rich foods like berries (all kinds), cruciferous veg (Brussels sprouts, broccoli, cauliflower), pomegranate, green tea, turmeric, oysters.

To help you kick-start and step into the **BODY and LIFE** you desire, I'd like to offer you a gift, go to**:** www.heidireboot.com and enjoy my **5 x Full Body Workouts for Beginners** and a **14-day Healthy Eating Plan** to get you feeling energised and strong.

Time Restricted Eating:

This is something that I believe in, and something worth trying. It gives your body time to 'spring-clean and repair' instead of permanently being in 'digestion mode'. The basic rule is - don't eat after dinner and leave at least 12-hours before you eat breakfast. An even more effective ratio is a 16-hour window at least three times a week - you finish eating by 8pm and then eat nothing until midday the following day. You're going to notice significant changes almost immediately. You'll feel lighter, more energetic and alert, less 'brain fog' and you'll sleep better. You can always adjust the number of days depending on how you feel and the results you're working towards. It's effective but not for everyone – not for pregnant women, the elderly, frail and infirm, children, people with eating disorders.

Healthy Fats:

Do you remember when we were told fats were the enemy? We all bought low-fat or non-fat foods given the option. News flash! Times have changed and now we know that fats (healthy fats that is) play an important role in our overall health.

Monounsaturated and polyunsaturated fats are the ones you should include in your diet.

They're found in avocados, nuts and seeds along with essential Omega-3 fatty acids found in oily fish (salmon, mackerel, sardines, anchovies) olives and olive oil. Eat some healthy fat with every meal, as it will make you feel more satiated for longer. I've been living in the South of France for over 15 years and I'm happy to say that the 'Mediterranean Diet' has been listed over and over again as the healthiest diet for us all. The 'mascot' of the 'Mediterranean diet' is olive oil. It's high in monounsaturated fatty acids. It can help raise the level of 'good' cholesterol in your body. The number one fat to lower your risk for heart disease is OLIVE OIL.

Unhealthy Fats:

Saturated fats should be limited to less than 6% of your calorie intake - that translates to about 120 calories, or 13 grams per day – on a 2,000-calorie daily diet. Saturated fats are found mostly in animal-based products (milk, butter, ice-cream, cheese, red meat, poultry).

However, saturated fats are part of your diet, so just choose wisely and enjoy them in moderation.

Protein:

Protein is a priority in your diet. There are 12 amino acids that create the protein building blocks of your body, 9 of which are essential. Protein plays a role in all the chemical reactions in your body along with the transport of oxygen in your blood and even the structure of your muscles, skin, hair and nails. I'm sure you can appreciate the importance of protein in your diet - try to eat some protein at every meal.

There are 2 types of protein – animal and plant. Animal protein, such as meat, fish, poultry and eggs, are complete proteins and contain all 9 essential amino acids. These are the building blocks of your body, they're essential, your body can't make them, that's why you have to get these 9 amino acids from your diet. There are also plant-based proteins which are often, but not always, incomplete proteins, such as soy, tofu, tempeh, hemp seeds and buckwheat. Quinoa is a complete plant protein. If you're vegan, all you need to do is combine plant proteins to create complete proteins. I often eat pumpernickel (dark bread) with almond butter for breakfast = a complete protein. Bean soup, grainy crackers and a sprinkling of mixed seeds for lunch = a complete protein. How about black rice with black beans and vegetables for dinner = complete protein. Hemp seeds are a good source of plant protein and can be added to your morning smoothie or sprinkled on your salad and they're also a good source of healthy fat.

The **minimum** of how much protein to eat is - take your weight in kgs and eat that many grams of protein per day (spread across 3 meals). If you weigh 60kgs, you eat, at least 60gms of protein each day. It's a good idea to mix it up – don't eat just animal protein – mix in plant protein too. The protein will help keep your blood sugar more stable, protein is necessary for your cells to repair and is also good for collagen production and detoxification.

Carbohydrates:

Carbohydrates are important because they provide your body with energy. They're not all equal though. Broccoli is a carb, and so is a cookie! You need to fill your plate with healthy carbs from unprocessed whole grains (quinoa, black rice, amaranth, buckwheat) colourful fruits, vegetables and beans (not too starchy) and avoid the unhealthy carbohydrates - white food (bread, potatoes, pasta, rice) and sugar.

You need to eat 6-8 servings of vegetables per day and 'eat the rainbow'. Choose low-sugar fruit like berries (all berries) kiwi and pomegranates (less sugar.) All other fruits, eat with some healthy fat (coconut/soy yogurt or almond butter) to avoid a spike in your insulin levels.

Metabolism:

Metabolism is the process by which your body converts whatever you eat or drink into energy. It's the rate at which you break down food. Your metabolism naturally slows down as you age, due to loss of muscle mass (keep reading for ways to avoid this decline!) in fact, it declines 10% each decade after the age of 20.

Your body needs energy for every function – from breathing, digestion, and circulation to brushing your teeth. The number of calories your body needs to complete these basic functions is called your basal metabolic rate. We all have a different basal metabolic rate determined by gender, age and body size. Besides your BMR, there are other factors that account for how many calories you burn in a typical day. Thermogenesis, which means the digestion and absorption of food and nutrients, accounts for about 10 percent. Physical activity contributes another chunk and is determined by how active you are and the intensity. Everything else is considered non-exercise activity thermogenesis (NEAT) which are all the small movements you do during the day like boiling the kettle, reading a book or driving a car… depending on the person, NEAT can account for 200-800 calories a day.

My clients complain that the number on the scale keeps creeping up and often, it's the hormonal changes that come with menopause that's to blame. The drop in estrogen levels signal the body to store more fat, especially around the belly. Yikes! That means that if you live a sedentary lifestyle, you'll gradually put on weight and be at risk for serious disease. The most effective way to increase and maintain your metabolism is by incorporating resistance training into your exercise routine (keep reading, I'll reveal more in Secret Step Six).

Your mindset, understanding and reasons WHY.

Once you understand what to eat to fuel your body and mind, it's important to know your **WHY?** Identify your motivation and attach a feeling for greater success!

WHY is good health and a healthy diet important to you at this time in your life?

- ______________________________
- ______________________________
- ______________________________

When you consciously choose what you eat for the health of your *whole* being, you start to make better food choices. You learn to appreciate and understand what to eat, when, and how much to fuel your body and mind so you feel healthier, fitter, calmer, more in control, confident, energised and alive.

Hey, I know it takes commitment, I've been doing this stuff for more than 30 years! Also, remember, you don't have to be perfect all the time; you're allowed treats now and then.

The reality is, it's SO worth it when your body feels strong, toned, and you have masses of energy from clean, healthy nutrition so you can experience everything you want to accomplish, each and every day.

Where are you now? On a scale of 1-10, where do you perceive the quality of your diet is today? (1 = I don't care, 10 = Excellent)

- ______________________________

What are your expectations and how would you like to look and feel?

- ______________________________
- ______________________________
- ______________________________

It's time to initiate the clear action steps to improve your diet to achieve and maintain a healthy body. Once you start seeing and feeling the changes, you'll feel inspired to continue with even more healthy eating habits going forward.

Start with **some immediate, short-term goals – next 12 WEEKS**

Write down 5 positive action steps you will commit too today to improve your diet for the next 12-WEEKS – connect with your **'WHY'** – it will help you stay committed.

1. I will ____
2. I will____
3. I will____
4. I will____
5. I will ____

It's time to clear out your fridge, throw away all the high fat, processed, high sugar and salt laden food in your refrigerator and kitchen cupboards.

Eating healthier can be challenging to start with, the best way to avoid the temptation of unhealthy foods is to keep them out of your house. Once you've cleared out, thrown away/or donated the foods you now know are damaging your body, you're ready to go shopping for the good stuff!

By stocking your refrigerator and cupboards with healthy choices, you're more likely to succeed in your goal toward a healthy, wholesome diet AND improved health!

The following are a few basic staple foods and ingredients on your shopping list…

Avocados

Yogurt (plant-based)

Blueberries

Canned sardines, salmon, mackerel

Beetroot

Green tea

Sweet potatoes

Leafy greens

Red/yellow peppers

Olive oil

Dark chocolate 75%+

Apples

Walnuts, almonds, brazil nuts

Tomatoes

Broccoli

Almond butter

Plant/nut milk & yogurt.

Coffee

Carrots

Red wine

Organic eggs

Buckwheat

Lentils

Coconut oil

Blueberries

Artichokes

Salmon

Seeds – chia, sesame, pumpkin, sunflower, linseed

Now you have a general outline of WHAT to eat and even WHEN to eat.

The most important and probably the most difficult change to make will be moving away from, and eliminating, all starch and sugar-laden foods from your diet.

What you'll notice is how difficult it is: sugar is a drug and you're going to feel the withdrawal symptoms and definite cravings. It takes time, so perhaps start by cutting out bread and sugary snacks.

Here are some ideas for healthy snacking:

- Chop up raw veggies like cucumber, celery, carrots, zucchini and cauliflower and put in a sealed box in the fridge, so you have a ready-to-go snack - dip in hummus or almond butter
- Same with fruit – wash, peel, slice or dice the fruit, so it's ready

before you get hungry – choose apple, pear, peach, watermelon, orange and berries - dip in yogurt or almond butter

- Handful of almonds, walnuts, 3 Brazil nuts (or any unsalted nut except peanuts)
- Celery with a tbsp of almond butter
- A cup of berries
- One hard-boiled egg
- Tomato and cucumber with olive oil, lemon juice and spices
- Pumpernickel bread with hummus & chopped tomato, salsa or cucumber
- Buckwheat rice cake with almond butter & berries or green apple
- Buckwheat rice cake with egg salad (egg, mashed avocado, olive oil, salt, pepper, paprika)

I would love to share with you one of my favourite cookbooks – **'Clean Eating Alice'- Eat Well Every Day.** It's packed with delicious, NUTRITIOUS, healthy recipes. I dip into these recipes ALL the time. You'll love them because they allow you to eat a nutrient dense, varied diet, full of interesting food and full of goodness. Each recipe is loaded with all the ingredients that promote good health, none of the bad stuff and all easy-to-prepare food anytime, all the time. No diet plans, just healthy, nutritious food! This cookbook will inspire and motivate you so that eating well will become so easy, you'll love the recipes which will inspire you to make lasting and sustainable change. Choose to eat a varied diet – full of nutritious ingredients and combinations so that you never feel bored with what's on your plate… be excited to try something new.

SECRET STEP SIX: ENERGIZE YOUR LIFE

Unlock your Best Body

When it comes to 'healthy aging' EXERCISE is going to be the closest thing to a miracle drug!

Along with a healthy, nutritious diet, regular exercise can slow age-related health problems, if not PREVENT them. It's time to boost your energy, wake-up your metabolism and have you moving that 'me' time to the top of your to-do list.

Make time for some kind of exercise every day.

Exercise protects your health, lifts your mood and increases your energy. It's one factor that's very tangible and controllable.

I remember how challenging it was on my own, trying to keep all the balls in the air. Life got a bit hectic as I tried to keep everything together for myself and my daughters. The only thing I could control and rely on was ME. I regularly put on my running shoes and headed out for a run in the park, and by the time I got back, I inevitably felt in control and powerful again.

Exercise helped me to cope.

Be smart: be kind to your body, treat it well and it will treat you well.

Once you start working out and exercising regularly, you'll notice improvements, not only in your body and your energy level, but in other areas of your life too. The discipline and commitment will make you feel in control and empowered. You'll have more patience, you'll feel calmer mentally, you'll show up in your relationships differently, less stressed.

You'll feel better about yourself and your self-confidence will blossom.

Create a manageable wellness routine. Your body is designed to move – it needs to for optimum health. Modern life – especially sitting in front of the computer screen, which is the norm for so many of us – is not helping us to look or feel the best that we can be. What you need is a well-rounded workout routine that mixes different kinds of exercise to build and maintain your bone health, heart health, muscle strength, balance, and coordination.

Posture. Another important, and often neglected subject, is posture. It's directly related to the muscle balance in your upper body, specifically your back, which is determined by your everyday lifestyle. So many of us sit at our computers all day or spend hours on our smartphone, keeping our upper back and neck in a rounded and forward position. Your posture and body language speak volumes. When you see someone standing with their shoulders back and down, chest lifted, do they look confident and self-assured? Do they look elegant and poised? Is their posture a reflection of how they feel, or is their posture influencing how they feel? You can shift your body in order to shift your mind.

Here's your sitting posture check:

- Sit up straight, away from the back of the chair
- Lengthen your spine, move your shoulders back and down

- Bring your chin in, eyes looking straight ahead, be aware of your body position
- Place both hands behind your head, lifting and lengthening your spine and opening your elbows wide and gently push your elbows outwards, back and down. Keep your shoulders down away from your ears
- Hold this wide elbow position for 7-8 seconds, then release and relax back in the chair
- Repeat this sequence every hour, gradually you'll start sitting with better posture and stop slumping at your desk.

Take a posture pause every hour!

When you're standing, stand tall. You'll feel better and look better, slimmer, even.

Here's your standing posture check.

- Stand up against a wall with your heels touching the wall
- Hold your head straight and tuck in your chin
- Stand with your shoulders back and touching the wall
- Knees straight, and tummy tucked in
- Straighten up, so you feel like there's a piece of string being pulled upwards out of the top of your head
- Step away from the wall and aim to maintain this body posture as you move through your day.

The Wonder Woman Power Pose!

Your posture is important and communicates to those around you in various ways. The challenge is when you're not feeling confident, you're on your back foot and you need a dose of 'fake it till you make it' - that's when the Power Posture Pose (the Wonder Woman) comes into play!

If you've got an important business meeting and need a quick confidence boost or you're about to give a presentation and you're waiting backstage, or even if you're going on a date and you're feeling a bit nervous, here's what to do:

- Stand with feet hip width apart
- Put your hands on your hips, shoulders back and down
- Chest lifted, long, tall neck and eyes looking straight ahead. This is your POWER POSTURE POSE!
- Now's the time for your 3 'I AM's' - e.g. I am capable, I am confident, I am beautiful!

Choose your own three, repeat them 3-4 times, drop your arms and **GO FOR IT!**

One more tip: Keep your heels and stilettos for a night out. Wearing heels every day is not good for your posture. They push the base of your spine forward, which over-arches your back and can change the way your backbone lines up. This puts pressure on the nerves, which causes back pain. High-heeled shoes also put more weight on your knees. Choose fashionable trainers or a low, chunky heel for daily wear.

The Three Components of Physical Fitness

There are three components to a well-rounded and effective exercise routine. All three can be incorporated into one workout:

- **AEROBIC** – Aerobic activities such as power-walking, jogging/running, cycling, swimming and your Zumba/aerobics class, work your cardiovascular system by raising your heart rate for an extended period of time making your heart stronger and more efficient at pumping oxygenated blood around your body. As you become more aerobically fit, you'll improve your endurance, stamina and all-round heart health.
- **RESISTANCE** – Resistance/strength training using dumbbells, weight-machines, bands etc.

Strength training using weights, bands, or just your own body weight (push-ups/crunches, sit-ups, planks and squats) are an important component of your exercise routine. As you build a strong body you create strength and stability around your joints which will help prevent injury.

We lose, on average, about 30% of our muscle mass between age 50 and 70. If you're inactive, you'll start to lose as much as 3% to 5% each decade after 30. Resistance training also helps build stronger bones to prevent osteoporosis and thin bones. It also stops you from shrinking as you age due to fragile, weak bones. About a 20% loss of bone density happens during the first five years after menopause.

Did you know that muscle burns more calories than fat? About 6 calories per pound of muscle compared to 2 calories per pound of fat. When you include resistance-training into your routine, you'll replace body fat with muscle which will increase your metabolism, even at rest, your body is actively burning calories due to the change in your body-composition. Resistance-training is an effective way to maintain a healthy body weight. Your posture will also improve with weight-bearing exercise – when you work specific muscle groups you can significantly improve your posture.

- **FLEXIBILITY** – Activities that develop flexibility are Pilates, yoga, stretching after exercise, martial arts, gymnastics and dance. Stretching can also help with reducing stress. Maintaining flexibility is an important component to overall wellness. It helps to avoid injury by maintaining correct movement around the joint, and also improves balance and coordination. If you were to accidentally slip and fall, you'd have the flexibility and strength to catch yourself along with the mobility to move and recover without stiffness, aches and pains.

Take a look at your lifestyle, does your routine include some form of exercise at least three times per week - a minimum of three and a half hours per week? Circle your answer

- Yes No

Does the exercise you do fit into all three components of a well-balanced exercise routine = aerobic, resistance and flexibility?

- Yes No

Let's create a vision around how you would like to look physically, how you want to feel, and why this is important to you. You'll radiate the vitality you feel with a stronger body, a body that you love and respect.

Where are you now? On a scale of 1-10, where do you perceive your level of fitness is today (1 = can't climb the stairs, 10 = Extremely active – feel at my best physically)

- ____

What is your present activity level? (circle what applies to you)

- I am **sedentary** – no exercise
- I walk the dog **occasionally**
- I play golf or cycle **once a week**
- I exercise **1 hour - twice** a week (group classes, gym, cycle, tennis, golf, swimming, running, power walking)
- I exercise **1 hour – two or three times** a week (group classes, gym, cycling, golf, tennis, swimming, running, power walking)
- I exercise **at least 1 hour four to five times** a week (group classes, golf, gym, cycling, HIIT, swimming, running)

What are your 3 favourite ways to stay active?

1____

2____

3____

What are 3 activities/types of exercise/sports you'd like to try?

1____

2____

3____

How would you like to look and feel?

1____

2____

3____

WHY is exercise, and being physically fit, important to you at this time in your life?

1____

2____

3____

What are 3 action steps you will do consistently and commit to (today) to improve your activity/fitness level?

1____

2____

3____

What are 3 things that you can do to make sure you stay motivated to execute your fitness plan?

1____

2____

3____

How will these commitments make you FEEL (this is your WHY) as you move into this next phase of your life?

1____

2____

3____

Here's an idea for you, when life gets a bit hectic:

I'm sure you're busy, and adding regular exercise along with some quality and needed 'me-time' is challenging. You're juggling work and/or family and there just doesn't seem to be enough hours in the day.

I totally get it!

What you need is a morning routine that you can do consistently and can maintain.... Actually, it's **HOW** you start your day.

Well, I've got **two** options for you: a 1-HOUR Morning Routine OR a 20-MINUTE Morning Routine. Many of my clients have adopted these morning routines and find them manageable, rewarding, and relatively easy to incorporate into their lifestyle on a daily basis.

1. **One-Hour-A-Day Morning Routine**. It's an inside-out, and outside-in morning wellness routine. It's manageable, structured and effective and could be exactly what you need and something you can commit to.

WAKE-UP!

- Spend 10 minutes meditation + gratitude + tea/coffee/celery juice/water with lemon.
- Spend 20 minutes doing aerobic exercise e.g. walk/jog around the block a few times, rebounding on a trampoline or pedalling on a stationary bike or get outside on your road bike.
- Spend 20 minutes doing weight-bearing exercises for your upper-body along with core-strength/abdominal exercises.
- Spend 10 minutes eating a healthy breakfast OR if you're doing time restricted eating, go have a hot/cold shower.

OR

1. **20-Minute-Simple Morning Routine.** This one is obviously shorter yet still effective. If you have limited time, this will work for you. Be consistent and commit to an inside/outside self-care, morning routine.

WAKE-UP!

- Spend 5 minutes meditating + gratitude + sip some water with lemon.
- Spend 10 minutes doing 4-5 full-body exercises - these are called compound exercises (using more than one body-part in each

exercise) repeat the exercises twice.

- Spend 5 minutes doing static, full body stretches.

The most important message I would like to pass on to you is this: make exercise a permanent fixture in your life, take care of your body by eating a healthy diet low in starch and sugar, move your body regularly and then let it rest and repair by getting quality sleep (7-9 hours).

You can achieve total wellness inside and out, start today.

Is it going to be one day OR DAY ONE?

I want you to feel the healthiest, happiest and most energized version of YOU!

By eating a **nutritious, clean diet** and adding **weight-bearing exercise**, you'll boost your energy, improve your mental health and feel stronger, leaner and more motivated, so you can enjoy a healthy, active life.

Let's start today!

Go to www.Heidireboot.com for your **FREE GIFT** ($497 Value)

My 5 x Full-Body Workouts for Beginners PLUS a 14-DAY Healthy Eating Plan – this will get you on the right path towards a healthy and strong body…you've got this!

SECRET STEP SEVEN: REIGNITE YOUR 'WOW' FACTOR

Radiant Skin, Fabulous Hair and Natural, Feel-Good Make-up

Sometimes it's as important to work from the outside in, as it is from the inside out - how we look on the outside often influences how we feel on the inside.

The inner journey you have taken so far has helped you reconnect with your inner strength, your talents and how accomplished and brilliant you are. You've tapped into your confidence and self-belief you've understood the importance of nutrition and exercise and now it's all about presentation and self-image. It's time to match the way you feel on the INSIDE to the way you look on the OUTSIDE by refreshing and updating your outer appearance and the way you present yourself to the world!

There's a dynamic, sexy, self-confidence that comes with great hair, radiant skin and light, luminous make-up that should never be underestimated. It plays a big role in our female identity, so now it's time you tap into your 'Inner Goddess' and watch her soar!

"True beauty is the flame of self-confidence that shines from the inside out" – Barrie Davenport

Are you ready to reconnect with that sexy woman you might have let slip down your 'to-do' list? She's still there you know, she's still part of you!

FEELING sexy starts on the inside and is reflected on the outside.

Client Case #7:

Stacey (name has been changed) was an accomplished research scientist, PhD and entrepreneur. She reached out to me for coaching. Stacey had created a new business and was ready to launch her online platform sharing Healthy Vegan Food. It included her hosting live cooking shows each week and naturally, she was the 'face' of her brand. The challenge she had was her inner wisdom and ultimately her self-belief were being crushed by lack of confidence directly related to the way she looked and her own image.

Stacey explained that she had never paid much attention to her outer appearance and now she understood that the way she presented herself needed to be a reflection of her 'Healthy Vegan Food' brand. She had no idea where to begin. She wanted to work with me on her 'outer' presentation and image. Stacey was intelligent, focused and self-assured and wanted her appearance to match her inner confidence and be a clear representation of her new business and brand. Stacey explained that she wanted to look healthy, naturally groomed and professional.

She wore her hair pulled back in a ponytail, soap and water were her skin cleansing routine and she had never worn make-up of any kind. After years in research, working in a lab, her skin was slightly sallow and dull, but her diet was fairly healthy, so the quality of her skin was quite good – it just needed some TLC and then a simple make-up routine with tips and techniques and best products to bring back the radiance and enhance her own natural beauty.

We brightened Stacey's hair colour and decided on a modern, versatile haircut that was easy for her to maintain and suited her busy lifestyle. We discussed her present image and style, her schedule, and then the goals for a practical wardrobe. We established what clothes she already had and what was missing, and then went shopping together to update and refresh her wardrobe.

Stacey launched her online business 'Healthy Vegan Kitchen' looking and feeling confident, beautiful and ready to conquer the world!

Radiant Skin

Your skin is a reflection of what's going on INSIDE your body.

What you eat has a direct impact on the quality and health of your skin.

The food you eat builds every cell in your body, so clean, nutrient rich food equals beautiful, radiant skin. Any inflammation inside your body, or in-balance in your gut, will be reflected on your skin.

Everything you have read in **Secret Step 5 - Nourish Your Body** - gives you exactly what to eat for a healthy, inflammation free body.

Here are 9 foods specifically for healthy, radiant skin:

- **Fatty Fish** – salmon, mackerel and herring are rich sources of Omega-3 fatty acids which will keep your skin supple and moisturised AND your hair glossy and healthy too. These Omega-3's can reduce inflammation which can cause red, itchy skin and also help your skin's sensitivity to the sun's harmful rays. Eat fatty fish twice a week.
- **Avocados** – a 'healthy fat' and wonderful for your skin health, keeping it flexible and smooth. They are also a good source of

vitamin E which protects your skin from damage and aging.

- **Olive oil** – keeps skin moisturised and reduces inflammation. Extra-virgin olive oil is rich in antioxidants to protect the skin – don't be afraid of 'extra' calories – olive oil is truly the most important unsaturated fat in your diet!
- **Walnuts & Brazil nuts** – another great source of essential fatty acids – your body doesn't make these essential fatty acids so they need to be added to your diet… walnuts and brazil nuts are rich in both Omega-3 and 6 and zinc which help heal your body and fight bacteria and inflammation. Try eating a handful of walnuts or 3 Brazil nuts as a mid-morning snack or crumbling them on top of your salad.
- **Sweet potatoes** – high in beta-carotene, which is an antioxidant, keeping your skin healthy by acting as a natural sunblock.
- **Dark chocolate** – at least 70% cocoa. Dark chocolate is rich in flavonoids that protect against sun damage, boosts collagen production, improves blood flow to the skin and increases skin density and hydration. OMG do you need any more reasons to enjoy dark chocolate?!
- **Red and yellow bell peppers** – are an excellent source of beta-carotene that your body converts into vitamin A – essential for healthy skin. They're also a great source of vitamin C which is necessary for creating the protein collagen which keeps your skin firm and strong.
- **Tomatoes** – are rich in carotenoids and a great source of vitamin C and lycopene, which is an antioxidant with natural sunscreen properties. Combine tomatoes with a source of fat like olive oil to

increase the absorption of carotenoids, which help prevent your skin from wrinkling.

- **Green tea** – helps your skin from damage and aging. It improves the moisture, thickness and elasticity of your skin.

The vitamins, minerals and antioxidants in foods like vegetables, fruit, and healthy fats are consistently associated with fewer wrinkles, thicker, smoother, and less age-related dryness in the skin.

Protect your skin from the sun every day with a broad-spectrum sunscreen to protect your skin from UVA and UVB rays. The UVA is the one that ages your skin and the UVB is the one that burns your skin. Apply a sun protection factor (SPF) of at least 30, applied 15 minutes before you go outside…every day (even on cloudy days). Wear UV-protection sunglasses (all year round) to protect the delicate area around your eyes as well as the eyes themselves. When you buy sunglasses check that they protect from the damaging rays, the ideal sunglasses should block 99-100 % of UVA and UVB rays.

Create a daily skincare routine – there are important steps to radiant, clear, glowing skin. You've just read the most important, which is your diet, an unhealthy, high starch and sugar diet will result in dull, dry, thin skin. Alongside SPF sun protection, a daily skincare routine is essential. It works on your skin from the outside, whilst your diet heals and builds healthy skin cells from the inside.

Here are the steps:

Step 1. Cleanse your skin – thoroughly remove make-up, dirt, oil and pollution by choosing a face cleanser that's gentle but effective.

Massage a small amount into your skin using your fingertips in a circular motion. The massage effects relax the muscles in your face and increase circulation. Then either with water or with a flannel or cloth, remove the cleanser taking away all the dirt.

Step 2. Exfoliate your skin – one of the best ways to brighten your skin both immediately and long term is by exfoliating. There are different ways to do that but they all do the same thing – they remove the skin's outer layer of dull, dead cells. The skin underneath is smooth, clear and reflects light so you have the radiance and a healthy glow that looks so beautiful.

You can use a cream or gel paste containing small granules – two to three times a week or a brightening liquid exfoliant with PHA (polyhydroxy acid) that improves overall skin tone and texture plus lightens dark spots using alpha hydroxyl acids.

Step 3. Hydrate your skin - with a layer of moisturiser. When skin is clear and smooth it reflects light, so instantly looks more radiant. You can choose a moisturiser with a broad- spectrum SPF 30 to shield from the damaging sun rays. When you use any kind of exfoliating acid on your skin, it makes it more sensitive to the sun and prone to sun damage and dark spots, so choosing a moisturiser with SPF or a make-up foundation with sun protection is important.

Step 4. For a fast fix – to get an instant boost of moisture and skin-plumping hydration, use a facemask. They're great before a special event or when your skin looks and feels lacklustre, you will see an immediate glow. You can buy a cream mask or the more popular and more effective are the hydrating facial sheet masks. You apply the facial sheet for about 15 minutes and then remove and rub into your skin any moisture left on the surface…fabulous!

Your Anti-Aging Skincare Routine:

Here is a morning and evening anti-aging skincare routine. The combination of vitamin C and retinol is an effective one-two punch for mature skin.

Vitamin C defends, protects and supports collagen production, while retinol renews skin cells and stimulates collagen. Used together, they reduce pigmentation and rejuvenate, replenish and brighten your skin.

Morning:

- Rinse your skin with cold water and pat dry (no need to cleanse – leave any natural oil on your skin that accumulated whilst you slept)
- Apply a **vitamin C** (antioxidant) moisturiser every morning to brighten and increase radiance and prevent uneven skin tone. It will soften fine lines, support collagen production and protect your skin from environmental stressors like free radical damage
- Next, apply a moisturiser with active ingredients to protect and hydrate your skin all day. Hyaluronic acid skincare products are also great as they hold the moisture in your skin (a moisture magnet)
- Add your SPF30 in the morning (very important if you're using a retinol cream at night)

Evening:

- Cleanse using a gentle gel/foaming cleanser to remove make-up, grime and grease, then rinse with water.

- Use a liquid or gel exfoliant three to four times a week to remove dead skin cells sitting on the surface of your skin containing PHA (polyhydroxy acid) that improves overall skin tone and texture plus lightens dark spots using alpha hydroxyl acids.
- Use a **serum with retinol** (the best is retinal+) It's a form of vitamin A and is effective for treating sun damage and dark spots, it also speeds up cell turnover, reduces fine lines and wrinkles, increases the production of collagen and stimulates new blood vessels in the skin.
- Apply a rejuvenating, quality night cream.

<u>My BEST anti-aging secret is – NO ADDED SUGAR in your diet.</u>

Collagen production naturally depletes as you age, but eating too much sugar and starch speeds this process up.

An occasional dessert is ok, but the sugar in processed foods, sugary drinks, cereals and sugary snacks, ages your skin dramatically by a process called glycation.

Glycation is when the sugar molecules in your system attach themselves to the fats and proteins in your body. The proteins in your skin (elastin and collagen) are the most prone to glycation. Once the sugar has attached to the protein it becomes brittle and you lose the plumpness in your skin, it becomes discoloured and weak causing wrinkles, sagging and loss of radiance. Starchy foods like **white rice, pasta, cereals, potatoes and white bread,** are also quickly converted to glucose and cause your blood sugar to shoot up and the glucose attacks the collagen in your skin.

Another thing to consider is that once glycation takes place, it can't be reversed. So, your best bet is to prevent glycation in the first place by eating a healthy diet that is low in sugar and starch. Aim to only eat sugars from natural sources like fruits and vegetables.

Here are 4 healthy lifestyle habits that can help make the most of the collagen you already have:

1. Eat a healthy diet high in nutrients including Vitamins A and C – Foods rich in **vitamin A** are leafy green vegetables (kale, spinach, broccoli), orange and yellow vegetables (carrots, sweet potatoes, pumpkin and other winter squash, summer squash) tomatoes, red bell pepper, cantaloupe, mango, beef liver, fish oils, eggs. Foods such as oranges, red peppers, kale, brussels sprouts, broccoli, and strawberries are all rich in **vitamin C.**
2. Follow a **daily skin care routine** that includes sunscreen SPF30 and topical retinol and vitamin C
3. Avoid skin **damaging UV rays** caused by excessive sun exposure.
4. Avoid smoking.

Bring back the radiance to the skin on your body.

TIPS

- Avoid highly perfumed soap as it will strip the natural oil from your skin – look for paraben free soap.
- Exfoliating your skin regularly improves circulation, breaks down cellulite, removes dead skin cells sitting on the surface and drains fluid – use a body brush, exfoliating mitt or apply a liquid/gel exfoliant on the dry areas of your body.

- Shave carefully and protect and lubricate your skin by using a shaving cream or gel – apply and wait 20 seconds for the hair to soften
- Use a moisture rich body cream or oil every day to help avoid dry skin.

Email me heidi@heidireboot.com for my favourite body cream – I've used it when working with supermodels on photoshoots, I use it myself all through the year – this product is one of my firm favourites. You'll understand why when you try it!

Fabulous Hair

This is an important subject for ALL women, let's all agree that our hair can directly affect the way we feel about ourselves – you know what they say about 'a bad hair day!' Yet there are so many pitfalls: the style, the length, and the colour are all part of our crowning glory. Our hair is so much a part of our identity, personality and self-image. I'd just like to go over some basics with you:

A Simple Hair Care Routine:

- Wash your hair 2-4 times per week, depending on hair texture and lifestyle. Don't think that just because you've done a workout and your hair is damp with sweat, you need to wash it – just blow-dry and keep that oily sebum on your scalp – it acts like a natural conditioner. Over-washing your hair (every day) disrupts the natural production of oil on your scalp by over-producing oil to compensate - giving you greasy roots and dry, crispy ends.

- Make sure you use a quality shampoo (you get what you pay for) especially if you're washing your hair several times a week – cheaper shampoos will just strip your hair of its natural oils. Remember you are predominantly washing the oil and dirt from your scalp, there's no reason to scrub the ends of your hair – it will cause your hair to split and break.
- Apply a quality conditioner and comb it through to the ends to evenly distribute the product (especially with long hair) then rinse thoroughly.
- If you have coloured hair or particularly dry, brittle hair, apply a deep moisturising hair mask and wrap your head in a towel for 7-8 minutes at least two to three times a week.
- Towel dry your hair gently… squeeze your hair with a towel, no rubbing required!
- Apply any styling products or heat/straightening protectants and style your hair.

Feel modern, sassy and confident with a refreshed hairstyle and/or colour, one that expresses exactly how you're feeling.

Your Hair Colour:

There are those who are embracing their grey hair after years of colouring and covering up their grey, and others who have coloured their hair for many years and will continue to do so.

It's important to choose a hair colour that complements your skin tone.

What is your skin tone – are you COOL, WARM or NEUTRAL?

COOL is blue, purple, grey, silver undertones

WARM is yellow, orange, peach, gold undertones

NEUTRAL is a mix of warm and cool

A simple way to know what colour your skin tone is – look at the veins on your forearm:

- If they are blue or purple, you have a COOL skin tone
- If they are green or olive, you have a WARM skin tone

Another simple way to uncover which skin tone you have is – look at your jewellery, does gold or silver jewellery look best on you?

- Silver jewellery is COOL
- Gold jewellery is WARM

You can also be a mix of warm and cool – you might have cool blue eyes and a warm, golden skin tone and so both gold and silver jewellery looks great on you OR you might have warm brown eyes with cool, pink skin and both gold and silver jewellery looks fab – don't get confused it's all beautiful.

Now you know your skin tone, you can choose a **complementary hair colour.**

Skin Tone	**Hair Colour**
Warm	warm auburn browns, warm reds (orange undertones) warm golden blonde
Cool	cool brown (blue undertones), cool red (purple undertones) cool ash blonde (silver undertones)
Neutral	choose any hair colour you like, but you'll find

you have a natural warm or cool tone that you lean towards and complements your skin tone.

Hairstyles to complement your face shape:

There are 6 different face shapes. Pull your hair off your face, stand in front of a mirror and see if you can identify your face shape from the list below:

DIAMOND – a narrow forehead, the widest part are the cheekbones and a narrow, slightly pointed chin.

Hairstyle - a great haircut would be a jaw length bob to increase width and soften the jaw. Straight hair looks great, as do soft curls with this face shape. Add volume at the jaw and not at the cheekbone area.

ROUND – no angles, full, round, circular face.

Hairstyle – perhaps stay away from a short, bob haircut as it accentuates the roundness. Choose slightly longer (shoulder-length) with some wispy layering to give you the appearance of a slightly sharper jaw and cheekbones. The hair length will give the appearance of a slightly longer face.

SQUARE – wide forehead with a matching wide jawline.

Hairstyle - this face shape looks good with a fringe to soften the forehead, choose a side-part giving softness and keeping the fringe longer at the outside corners and rounded. Wear your hair slightly longer and softly layered to soften the jawline

OBLONG – a mix of an oval and a square. The length of the face is twice the length of the forehead across. Fullness in the cheeks with no angular cheekbones or chin.

Hairstyle - add volume to the cheekbone area by soft layering that you can blow-dry giving width to balance the length of the face. A fringe looks great on an oblong face. Keep hair length no longer than your shoulders and add volume with layers. If your hair is too long, it will make your face look longer

HEART – the forehead is wider than the jaw, wider cheekbones and a slightly pointed chin.

Hairstyle - you want a hairstyle that decreases the width of the forehead and increases the width of the jaw area. A soft bob that has some layering at the jawline. A side part is best to break up a wider forehead.

OVAL – equally proportioned, no angles and very symmetrical

Hairstyle - any hairstyle suits this face shape, perhaps add an angle with a blunt, shortcut bob (jaw length).

4 Tips for Thinning Hair:

- All-one-length hairstyles are great; they trick the eye and make the hair look thicker and fuller. A bob haircut (jaw length or skimming your shoulders) and a soft fringe will also disguise thinning hair.
- Don't wash your hair every day – just rinse and add a lightweight conditioner to the ends.
- Don't over-style your hair (helmet hair) – create a more tousled, flirty and modern look. As you finish blow-drying, flip your hair upside down and spray (at arm's-length) a texturizing spray, run your fingers through hair at the root and then flip your head up and

let your hair fall naturally.

- Don't use 'shine sprays' – you want shine back in your hair, but these sprays contain silicone which gives your hair shine at first but in fact, dries out your hair…better to use a deep conditioning treatment once a week to restore the shine.

Natural, Feel-Good Make-up

Get ready to refresh and create an easy everyday make-up routine that suits you and your lifestyle, plus tips on how to take your make-up from daytime natural, to head-turning evening glamour.

Here are your simple steps for every day, natural make-up

1. Apply a primer to even out the texture of your skin and create a base for long-lasting make-up.
2. Choose a tinted moisturiser as your foundation with SPF20 or a lightweight foundation that illuminates your skin by reflecting the light – avoid heavy, matt foundations that give you a flat, mask like appearance.
3. Apply a cream, or liquid concealer one shade lighter than your natural skin colour. Dab with your ring finger a small amount of concealer on the inner corner of your eye (which is the darkest part of your face) then along your bottom lash-line and on your eyelid, blend gently with your finger or a concealer make-up brush.
4. Take your large, fluffy, powder brush and apply a lightweight, translucent powder all over your face and eyelid area to set your foundation and concealer.
5. Colour and shape your eyebrows with either an eyebrow pencil, coloured paste or eyebrow powder using an eyebrow brush.

6. Line your top lashes with a dark powder e.g. dark chocolate brown, black, charcoal grey, navy blue, deep plum. Use a very short bristled make-up brush so you can concentrate the colour when applying on the lash-line.
7. With a black or dark brown pencil or liquid eyeliner, deepen the colour on your top lashes by drawing a line as close to your lashes as possible and extend slightly outwards at the corners.
8. Apply mascara to your top lashes and a small amount to your lower lashes (optional). Choose a mascara that gives you the lash-look you want, which is ultimately determined by the brush applicator. Some brushes give you volume, others will build length, a plastic comb/brush applicator prevents clumping.
9. Choose your blush colour, either a warm, apricot/peach or a cool, coral/pink, and apply to the middle and top of your cheekbones. Blend from the middle of the 'apple' of your cheek (the fullest part when you smile) up towards your temples. Add a touch of blush across the top of your forehead close to your hairline, and then dab a little on your chin (in fact, all the places that the sun would naturally land on your face).
10. Then finally, using a lip pencil that matches your natural lip colour, outline your lips, smudge gently with your finger to soften the line, then apply your favourite lip colour and finish with a dab of lip gloss in the centre of your bottom lip and the middle portion of your top lip line.

Now you have this simple, practical knowledge and know-how, go-ahead and reignite your sexy, boost your self-confidence, and **Get-Your-Glow-On**!

3 Easy Steps to go from Daytime Natural to Evening Glamour!

1. Apply the same colour eyeshadow that you used along your lash line, to the crease of your eye-socket, blend with a soft make-up brush and then deepen the colour along the upper lashes and the outside corner and blend creating a smoky eye. Take a sparkly white eyeshadow and apply a small amount on the innermost corner of your eye to make your eye pop.
2. Apply more blush, deepening the colour, and then brush a little on your eye-socket bone.
3. Apply a stronger colour on your lips and then a gorgeous lip gloss – a quick tip: dab your sparkly white eyeshadow in the middle of your lower lip and the top 'peaks' of your upper lip – it creates the illusion of fuller lips and the light will dance across your mouth Vavavoom!

NOW GO and ENJOY, CELEBRATE and FEEL FABULOUS!

SECRET STEP EIGHT: EMBRACE YOUR PERSONAL STYLE

PERSONAL STYLE

This is many things: it's how you dress, do your hair, decorate your home, act on a date, drive your car, treat a friend, do your job and make your choices.

First 10 seconds count (actually, a study was done and it's 7 seconds!). People look at your body language, eye contact, what you say or don't say in the first 7 seconds of meeting you – and make a judgement call. So as first impressions count, let's uncover and refresh your personal style, decide what you like and what best expresses the way you want to look and feel.

Mindset

On a scale of 1-10 - How important is the way you present yourself to others? (1= totally unimportant) (10 = I like to showcase the very best version of me)

- ____

How will changing your outer appearance affect the inner you?

- ____
- ____
- ____

Finding your style

Analyse your present style.

Look at your 'go-to' outfits – what you like and don't like.

Look at your wardrobe and diagnose what you see: is there plenty of colour? Mostly black and white? Any patterns? Is it full of simplicity and basics? Have you got duplicates of the same items?

When working with my clients on their personal image and style, I have two suggestions to **collect inspiration**

- Online – look on Instagram and Pinterest and collect photos and styles you like and create your own Pinterest Board.
- Magazines – tear out photos of clothes and 'looks' that you love, then create a 'fashion board' for yourself. You'll see your favourite trends, colour palette and vibe guiding your ideas, styles and the looks that you can recreate.

Be authentic, don't follow trends...CONFIDENCE always looks good!

On a scale of 1-10, how would you rate your present, personal style? 1 = I definitely need to revamp 10 = my style represents exactly who I am

- ______________________________
- ______________________________
- ______________________________

Describe in 3 words your present style? e.g. – casual, relaxed, classic, chic, sporty, edgy, trendy, feminine, sexy,

- ______________________________
- ______________________________
- ______________________________

What 3 colours do you wear most often?

- ______________________________
- ______________________________
- ______________________________

What do you think needs updating in your wardrobe?

- ______________________________
- ______________________________
- ______________________________

Choose 3 parts of your body you like the most? (don't dodge this question!)

- ______________________________
- ______________________________
- ______________________________

If you were to update your image and style, what is your signature item that you wouldn't give up?

- ____
- ____
- ____

As you move into this new phase, what 3 words best describe how you would like to look and feel – your ideal style and image?

- ____
- ____
- ____

What 3 immediate changes could you make to revamp and refresh your wardrobe?

- ____
- ____
- ____

Your Personal Style Plan

It's important to understand how to dress to flatter your own specific body shape. When you focus on the areas of your body you like and your 'best bits' you will create a wardrobe of clothes you love to wear and stop wasting money on clothes that don't look good on you. It's time to show off your assets and look at your personal style and how it relates to your present life, style and image.

Let's start with your body shape and what styles suit what shape.

Decide which shape below most closely represents your body shape – you might be a mix of two, and that's quite possible…just read guidelines for both.

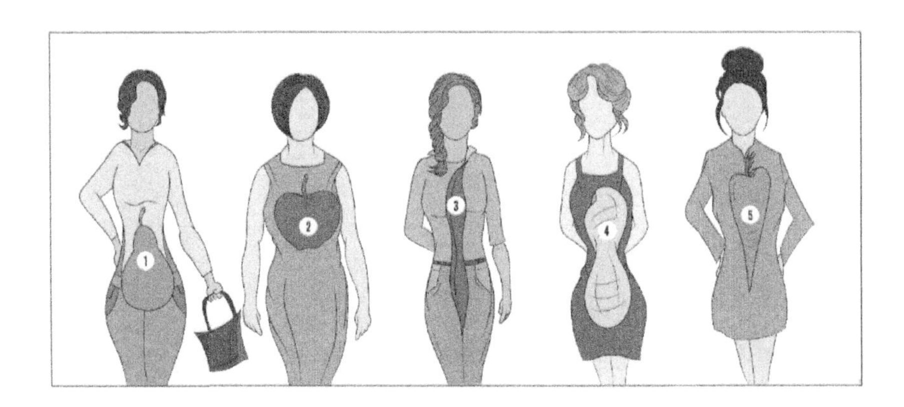

1. The Pear (the triangle)

Curvy hips, thicker thighs and a full bottom are the key characteristics of the pear-shaped body. The pear-shaped woman often has a smaller bust, narrower shoulders {compared to her hips} and a defined waist.
My advice: Balance your proportions by drawing the eye to your upper body with pretty collars, scarves, great earrings and chunky necklaces. Blouses, shirts and knitwear with detail on the chest or shoulders adds balance to a smaller bust and shoulders. Choose darker colors on your

lower body. Wear jackets with structured shoulders. Layer on your upper body.

2. The Apple (the circle)

Rounder shoulders and a flat bottom describe this body type. This apple-shaped woman has a larger bust and fullness around her middle. She has good legs that take centre stage when dressing.

My advice: With the tendency to carry weight around your middle, choose clothes that skim that area. Don't automatically buy huge baggy tops to hide your tummy – choose items that create some structure and shape to your upper body. Choose a hip length jacket - single breasted. Choose fine knit sweaters, not chunky knit. Always go for a V-neck rather than a round neck, so your larger bust doesn't look like a shelf. Show off your legs with slim trousers, leggings and skirts. Another option is to wear all one colour on your upper and lower body, then accent with fab shoes or a long tunic style jacket.

3. The String-Bean (the rectangle)

Your hips and shoulders are much the same width. The goal with this body type is to create curves.

My advice: Choose clothing that creates the illusion of curves. Create a waistline when you can with belts, ruching or wrap-around items. Add chunky knitwear, layering, boxy short jackets with structured shoulders and double-breasted jackets. Choose wrap dresses and add a small shoulder pad where possible. Look for styles that fit at your waist and flare out at the bottom (a skirt or trousers) to create curves.

4. The Peanut (the hourglass)

This body shape is well proportioned, with the shoulders and hips well-balanced. The hourglass body has a fuller bust with a defined waistline and round, curvaceous hips.

My advice: Choose clothes that hug and skims your curves. All jacket styles work on this body shape, and adding a belt to a longer jacket highlights the waistline. You can wear almost anything you want because your body is well-proportioned.

5. The Carrot (the inverted triangle)

This body shape has wide shoulders and a full bust. The lower body is slim with a narrow waist and hips. Along with this body shape comes great legs. The goal here is to balance the upper and lower body.

My advice: Choose jackets with soft fabric that mould to your upper body to soften your shoulders. No layering on your upper body. Choose skirts and trousers that are full and more fluid on your lower body. This body type has slim legs, so choose fun, A-line and circular skirts to the knee. The goal is to accentuate your lower body, while softening your shoulders and upper body.

Your Best Colours:

Finding 'your' colours, the ones that complement and enhance your skin, hair and eye colour, is a powerful tool. Add them to your wardrobe, amongst your neutrals, and watch what happens! You're going to hear "Oh WOW, you look radiant" or "Are you in love, you're glowing!".

You analysed and decided on your skin tone in the previous chapter, so let's go!

Warm skin tone = your best colours have a warm undertone. Choose a red with an orange undertone, coral, orange, tan and gold all look great and have natural warmth. Choose a yellow with a warm gold undertone. Your best green is with a yellow undertone, e.g. olive or moss green. Choose a creamier white rather than pure white. Chocolate brown, blue, burgundy, grey, taupe and camel are all best with a warm yellow undertone.

Cool skin tone = your best colours have a cool undertone. Your best red will have a blue undertone. Your blues, greens, yellows, browns, greys, pinks and purples look great with a cool undertone. Choose pure, crisp white to complement the coolness in your skin.

Every colour has a warm or cool undertone, so the key to your success is to lean towards the version that matches your own skin tone.

Your Top 10 Wardrobe Essentials

You can create a versatile, flattering wardrobe with your current clothes, identify any gaps, go shopping for any missing essentials and then embrace your newfound confidence to try new things and feel fabulous. With these 10 items you'll find ways to refresh and update your wardrobe and having a pared-down, capsule wardrobe, it truly takes the guesswork out of getting dressed each day! With these 10 items on hand, you'll always know what to wear for almost any occasion: a job interview, workday, date night, a PTA meeting, gym/yoga, or running errands. And the best news is, you can count on these items being in style for several years to come.

Slip into something that represents the way you want to look and

feel, as the new YOU!

1. Denim. First on the list has to be jeans. They're an everyday staple that can be worn to virtually every occasion. Select a variety of washes, depending on your body shape, choose a light wash, medium wash, dark wash, and also a black jean. Choose from a set of core styles that suit your shape slim fit, straight leg, flare, skinny and cropped, along with low, medium and high-waisted styles. Invest in a few quality pairs that will last.

2. A classic blazer. Structured outerwear is one thing you can always count on. The key is to look for a blazer that suits your body shape and your lifestyle. Do you need something formal for the office? Do you need single or double-breasted? Do you want one you can layer with any top underneath? Remember: it's all about versatility, and investing in pieces that do it all.

3. Basic tee-shirts and tank tops in black, white, beige, grey, navy. Great under jackets, cardigans and sweaters. When can't you wear a white t-shirt? It should be a staple in every woman's wardrobe. Pair a white tee with your favourite pair of jeans, a skirt, a great jacket, or with casual leggings. Any way you style it, a basic tee/tank is a must.

4. Ballet flats and heels. We all have that one pair of flats that work with everything (from jeans and a tee-shirt to a simple dress) and can be worn from work to drinks to weekend casual. A pair of simple ballet flats will carry you through the seasons — and years. The same applies to a great pair of heels. Invest in a quality pair that you feel comfortable and confident in, and can work across your wardrobe.

5. A beautiful blouse. You can never go wrong with a blouse. A crisp, classic white, a vibrant patterned signature piece or a soft silk option – choose one that is versatile and can be effortlessly styled for both work and play.

6. A signature style dress. It's an essential and the ultimate "I have nothing to wear" throw-on-and-go item. It's that one piece that solves all the indecision. Choose your signature style and a dress that you feel beautiful, comfortable and sassy when you wear it. Long and flowing, short and hugging, wrap around and soft or whatever style you love…one that you can style for any occasion.

7. A classic coat. A coat is an investment piece, as are your boots. Keep the style and shape of your coat fairly classic and it can last you for decades. Your coat is a loyal friend, that item in your wardrobe that takes you to work, the outdoors at weekends and the mountains in winter – Take proper care of it, and it will care for you in return.

8. Workout gear. Exercise and fitness are obviously an important part of your lifestyle going forward, so stock up on great exercise clothing – it will keep you motivated, feeling, and looking good on your fitness journey to a strong healthy body. Choose comfortable, mix & match pieces that are flattering and supportive. 'Athleisure' (a mix of athletic and leisure clothing) gear is popular and can be worn throughout the day not only to exercise… select leggings, bra tops, tee-shirts and soft jackets that wash-and-go… they need to keep up with YOU!

9. A pair of boots. Along with your coat, your boots are an investment piece…you definitely get what you pay for. Choose from high riding-style boots, knee-high, mid-calf or ankle boots in black or brown. Look after them and they will serve you well.

10. Soft knitwear. You're going to love the comfort and versatility of soft knitwear. Trousers, tank tops, dresses, skirts, tee-shirts, sweaters and cardigans (long and short) all gorgeous, comfy, soft knitwear. For every body type – just go for it. They can be mixed in, worn under or on top, and will wrap around you like a huge hug when you need it most. Choose any colour and feel loved and super comfortable. They are practical for travel and roll-up in your bag as your firm friend or back-up plan.

Accessories

Accessories can transform an ordinary outfit into an extraordinary outfit in simple but significant ways. You can create a signature style with accessories and really make an outfit your own.

Perhaps you're that person who always wears a stylish statement shoe – think colour, print and style (doesn't have to be a heel). A printed flat or a wedge heel can add personality and style to a casually thrown together outfit, or be the lead role in a simple ensemble.

Or maybe you're that someone who always has a great hat, one for every occasion. Your hats are your signature and a reflection of who you are!

Maybe you love bags and your personal style includes a fabulous and fun bag collection. You could add a pop of colour to your outfit with a great bag, sling a satchel or tote bag across your body or add texture, style and personality with every bag in-between.

How to Effortlessly Transition your Outfit from Day to Night

Daytime Ease to Night-time Ready: You're a fabulous, multitasking, intelligent woman and need to be ready for anything. That means your clothes need to be versatile, they need to reflect your image and keep up with you and your lifestyle.

Let's take basic items that you most likely have in your wardrobe - a pair of jeans, a white t-shirt and a classic blazer, then transition the outfit from day to night using **just accessories.**

Daytime Ease:

Morning AM - Start with jeans (any colour), flat shoes, white t-shirt, a colourful silk scarf tied at your neck, a classic blazer, a long chain bag across your body, medium size hoop earrings, and a pair of stylish sunglasses.

Night-time Ready:

Evening PM – slip on some heels, take your scarf and thread it through the waistband of your jeans to make a belt, add a pair of statement earrings and a stack of bracelets, put the chain strap of the belt inside the bag to create a clutch and off you go!

Fashion to Fit Your Lifestyle

Here are the 4 aspects of your life that you should consider before you refresh and update your wardrobe. Once you see how your lifestyle is divided, and the time spent in each, it will be helpful to review and then guide you.

- Family - at home with loved ones.

- Professional - at work or formal work environment.
- Active - outdoors doing physical activity, gym/exercising, or playing sport.
- Social - time with friends or social events.

Your lifestyle will dictate your wardrobe needs, a wardrobe full of casual clothes isn't going to work if you spend the majority of your time in a formal, corporate work environment. if you're a busy Mum juggling family, a yoga class, and mealtimes you're going to need a comfortable, practical, and versatile wardrobe with a faithful LBD (little black dress) for those well-earned sneaky nights out!

Decide what percentage of your time you spend in each area:

Area:	**Percentage:**
Family____________________	________________
Professional _______________	________________
Active____________________	________________
Social____________________	________________

Make small changes

It's also important to try new things – to step out of your comfort zone. How about trying a new shape of jeans - boyfriend jeans instead of skinny, a flare instead of straight-leg? Try a wrap dress (short or long) to create a different silhouette instead of a slip/shift dress. How about palazzo pants or a pleated skirt instead of a cigarette pants or pencil skirt?

The most important message is to dress in a way that makes you feel **happy, confident and fabulous**. How you present yourself on the outside can change your mood and have a direct impact on how you feel on the inside. Experiment with colour instead of sticking with a neutral palette. There are no rules, age is just a number, so let loose and express your fabulosity!

Here are my 10 Ways to Feel Young at Any Age:

1. **Find and follow your passion**. When you lose yourself in something you love, it will bring energy, confidence and a radiance to your life. If you haven't found your passion yet, don't feel pressured, just be curious and try new things and you'll soon find something you love.
2. **Put on loud music when your bath is running or your shower is warming up, and dance naked around your bedroom.** Now this is a total 'feel good' moment – any age, anytime, alone or with your partner. Choose your favourite soundtrack, add a quick shake of your 'money-maker!' and you'll enjoy freedom, and plenty of laughter leaving you feeling young, sexy and alive!

3. **Make exercise a permanent fixture in your life.** Healthy habits like regular exercise give you a feeling of accomplishment and will protect your health, lift your mood and increase your energy.
4. **Indulge your inner child... trampoline park, roller-skating, paint a mug.** Find ways to feel playful, cheeky and flirtatious – don't hold back when you get the chance to be child-like and fun.
5. **Develop and nurture your creativity.** Express yourself through creativity. It might be painting, music, cooking, dancing, playing an instrument etc. the joy will radiate from within and the world will see your joy.
6. **Be adventurous.** Find ways to step outside your comfort zone by trying new things or travel to places 'off-the -beaten track' and have an adventure.
7. **Don't let fear, failure or criticism hold you back.** Live each day in-the-moment and stop being preoccupied with people's opinion or your past and the future.
8. **Meditate for 10 minutes every day.** It will improve brain health, protect your cells from aging and recharge your body – you're going to glow!
9. **Get enough sleep.** Sleep is vital to keeping your memory sharp and your mood and energy high.
10. **Learn to love yourself.** Know you are enough just the way you are, when you love yourself, the world will love you back.
11. **Laugh as often as possible.** Smile, and laugh with sexy abandon. Laugh at yourself, be silly. Enjoy every moment.

Design the life you love!

Inspirational Friends

I'd like to finish this book with two very inspirational stories - both written by best friends of mine, both went through their own **'Frightened to FABULOUS'** journey.

The reality is, we ALL have our own version of challenge and victory, and it can happen numerous times in life. The most important factor is we power forward, we choose to 'grab the rope' and haul ourselves out of the dark into the light!

In their own words:

Remember my friend Sue - early section of this book? Here's a quick reminder:

One day as I waited to pick up my girls from school, I felt a tap on my shoulder, and I turned to see the most gorgeous smiling face and the voice of an angel asking if I was American, and shall we go for coffee with the children? It was like a gift from above! Her name was Sue. She was from California and had three children of similar ages to my girls.

This friendship was instant, valuable and it truly saved me.

This is her story of Frightened to FABULOUS.

<u>Sue Corti</u>

Sue and I met outside the school gates, we have remained best friends for the last 20+ years.

The Race

The first time I heard the phrase "Cut to Cure" I was overwhelmed with emotion. In a routine yearly visit, a lump on my thyroid was discovered, followed by a biopsy, a wait for results and then a call that I took on speaker while driving my 12-year-old daughter to school. The doctor wanted me to come in to get the results. Never a good sign. My heart raced as my husband and I were seated across from the doctor, just like in the movies.

"Cut to Cure", and then what?

Cancer survivor, what does that even mean?

I was a stay-at-home mom with my eldest heading off to college that year. I had recently taken up the sport of triathlon and was fitter than I had ever been. Post thyroidectomy and radioactive iodine treatment, I was impatient to get back to racing. The race was to benefit cancer support. I raised funds with a passion and, 6 months post op, placed first in my age group.

Meanwhile, that same year, my Dad was diagnosed with metastatic kidney cancer and treatment wasn't going well. Despite being the strongest man I knew and fighting like hell, he lost his battle in those same 6 months.

I had begun my triathlon journey with sprint races, less than 1 hour of swim, bike and run. Slowly I had built up the distance to 1/2 Ironman. I thought a full Ironman was craziness. Unfathomable to swim 2.4 miles, bike 112 and then run 26.2 miles, a full marathon! Not for me, no thank you.

My Dad was an athlete and had always been so proud of my racing. What was I waiting for? I signed up for my first Ironman the following year. I had no idea how hard it would be.

Six months out from my Ironman, I was still getting my thyroid meds sorted out, and was called back after a routine mammogram. Breast cancer? Two cancer diagnosis' in fourteen months and losing my Dad in between! I chose to have a bilateral double mastectomy with reconstruction.

This time surgery was more complicated, recovery took longer, and my dreams of racing an Ironman in honour of my dad seemed impossible. I could barely lift my arms overhead, and tears filled my goggles the first time I tried to swim. I felt like a turtle spinning my arms. I was crushed, but still determined. I looked at the calendar. I had 7 weeks until Ironman, was I crazy to try?

I had read a quote that resonated with me:

You have two lives, the second of which begins when you realise you only have one.

I was beginning to see what it meant to be a survivor. It's not just getting cancer, losing my dad, getting another cancer, it's everything that life throws at you. It's taking control of that one thing that you can control and running towards it, even if you might fail.

Seven weeks later, I completed Ironman Mont-Tremblant in Canada in August 2014 for my dad and me. The next year I trained to race Ironman Coeur D'Alene and qualified for the World Championships in Kona, Hawaii.

It was truly a dream I had dared to dream it was a long hard day in Kona, but it was my victory lap and tears flowed as I ran toward the finish line to hear the iconic words, **"Susan Corti, you are an Ironman!"**

Alice Howe

Alice has been a best friend of mine for many years (20+) Our daughters met at pre-school in Malibu when they were six months old, and our families have stayed in touch ever since.

This is her story of *Frightened to FABULOUS.*

The Fire

It had been five years since my devastating divorce, it felt like a bomb had been dropped in the centre of my life, shattering the foundations of all I knew.

But I survived, I did it. Now I had a toolbox loaded with experience, I had my kids, family, friends, a business, my talent, my gifts, and my house!

Nov 8 2018, I was living in Malibu with my youngest daughter. After my divorce we stayed in the family house idyllically nestled in the Malibu hills.

Those typical, warm, blustery Santa Ana winds were swirling strongly that day as we left the doctor's office. It was unsettling, it only takes a spark and those winds can spread fire throughout the area, in minutes. The trees, bushes and terrain were dry and dense throughout Malibu, so perfect tinder, for a mighty bonfire!

Something made me rush home, the dogs were alone, and our house was susceptible!

The winds kept getting stronger, soon 70 miles per hour. We listened to the radio and watched the news, a variety of fires were already burning, but we were safe, all of them under control…that was, until they weren't!

Very quickly it went dark in Malibu. It was late afternoon when I looked at my watch, an enormous, toxic, dense, cloud of ash had moved in and we needed a flashlight to round up the dogs and bring them inside to safety.

Already exhausted from a long day, I put a bandana across my face to protect my lungs and went outside to move everything away from the house. I filled the trash cans with water and pulled them close by, ready to dowse any flames near the house. Back inside, more bad news, the largest fire was getting closer, I called my ex, he had an art studio on the property, his giant sculptures, ready for shipping to customers, were sitting in the studio, he was in Germany on business. I was frightened, but on autopilot, I asked him "what can I save, if we have to evacuate the house!"

He said "grab my hard drive" it was the size of a car battery. I covered my face, put my head down, walked against the 70 mile an hour wind, in the dark, across the property and found it. The car was full of computers, documents, few clothes, photos and dog food.

We were ready.

We sat through the night praying, trying to design a plan B, always hoping the wind would change direction and our house would be saved.

Morning came, I could just see the other houses through the thick smoke, then I saw the fire, the flames were huge, people were screaming. I said, "that's it, we're out of here now!"

"Everyone in the car" I looked back at my house one last time and then drove down the drive, I left the gate wide open for the fire department, but they never came, my heart was so tight in my chest, my face wet with tears.

We drove to Santa Monica to escape the fires, the only road out of Malibu was packed with bumper-to-bumper traffic, thousands of frantic people all facing the same trauma.

My daughter and I finally arrived in Santa Monica at my ex-husband's apartment, he was in Germany. No dogs allowed, thankfully they made an exception!

We were homeless, we didn't know anyone here in Santa Monica.

Three days later my friend called from Santa Barbara, desperate for news of our safety: "come here" she said, "the community here is amazing, the hotel has space for you and the dogs!"

It was the best news we had in days, so we moved.

In Santa Barbara we felt safe we had friends, other kids, and the hotel treated us well.

I reached out to family and friends in Brazil to tell them we were safe.

Malibu was in lockdown, no one allowed in or out. We waited for news every day, the 'hot spots' were still burning everywhere, we could see it at night from Santa Barbara, waiting and waiting to find out if we had lost everything or not.

One evening I got a call from my friend in Brazil, she was head of TV Globo News, a very important National television channel. She said "we're sending a crew to cover the fire, they're going to Malibu, we want you to go with them to your property, they can go through the police barriers with the media documents, you can go and see your house" I said "Yes I'm in"

The day came and I had no idea what I was going to find, how I was going to feel, I drove for an hour thinking how to prepare my mind, I called my doctor: he said, "you have courage Alice, you can do it."

I met with the crew at the gas station at the bottom of the hill, I said "listen, I may faint or cry," they said "no worries we are here for you."

I prayed, "Dear God, walk with me."

Driving up the hill it looked like we were on another planet, flattened, total devastation, dead wildlife everywhere.

At the gate, my heart sank, "My trees! My birds!"

I was counting with my eyes what might still be alive, the art studio by the gate looked like a torn, metal can…then the shock hit me, the void that was once my house, everything was gone, just ashes.

At that moment I closed my eyes, in my mind I walked to my front door, just like I'd done for 21 years. I had the house inside of me, I knew where everything was, the draws in the kitchen, the bathroom, my kid's bedrooms, my closet, I could sit in the living room and look at my paintings and the sunshine poring through the windows, I remember my babies crawling, birthday parties, sleep-overs, the sounds of the house, friends for dinner.

I knew then that every single thing was inside me forever.

Yes, I'd lost everything, I only had the clothes on my body, but my house and my memories lived in my soul.

I was alive, my kids and my dogs too!

A voice in my head whispered "my house is my body."

There's nothing more empowering than that.

I'm free, free to create a new amazing life.

Heidi says:

'ROCK WHAT YOU'VE GOT'

"Let your intelligent, fearless, authentic-self sit centre stage, be the leader in your life, shine bright, let your confidence show."

It's time to put yourself at the top of your to-do list!

www.heidireboot.com